COLOR BY OVERPRINTING

DONALD E. COOKE

COLOR BY OVERPRINTING

A complete guidebook in the art and printing techniques employing transparent
inks in multiple combinations. Illustrated with 495 three- and four-color groupings
of eleven basic inks, plus 44 pages of pictorial application of the medium.

Bourges, Inc., *art materials*
Bensing Brothers and Deeney, Inc., *ink research*
National Advertising Manufacturing Company, *printing*

*Fully annotated for reference of artists, printers, engravers, art directors and
editors in the book, magazine, advertising, and graphic arts fields generally.*

THE JOHN C. WINSTON COMPANY • Philadelphia • Toronto

FIRST EDITION

Made in the United States of America

CONTENTS

LIST OF ILLUSTRATIONS

LIST OF MANUFACTURERS

Typography: *Text*—Photocomposition on Intertype Fotosetter by Westcott & Thomson, Inc., Philadelphia.

                     Color chart pages set on Linotype by North American Composition Company, Philadelphia.

Paper: *Text*—Pastelle white antique, basis 80, manufactured by Strathmore Paper Company, West Springfield, Massachusetts.

                     Inserts—The Reader's Digest section: Warren's Olde Style, white antique wove, basis 70; coated paper inserts: Warren's Lustro Gloss, white, basis 100. Manufactured by S. D. Warren Company, Boston, Massachusetts.

Engravings: Letterpress engravings made by Philadelphia-Weeks Engraving Company, Philadelphia.

Inks: Transparent offset, letterpress and flexographic inks formulated by Bensing Brothers and Deeney Sales Company, Philadelphia.

Presswork: *Text* printed by offset on a Harris two-color press, Model LTL, 42 x 58.

                     Inserts printed letterpress on Miller two-color press, Model TW, 21 x 38.

                     Cover printed by offset on a Harris single-color press, Model LTN, 22 x 34.

                     All presswork by National Advertising Manufacturing Company, Philadelphia.

Cloth: Roxite Blubak CL-5888 manufactured by Holliston Mills, Norwood, Massachusetts.

Binding: Full cloth binding by Haddon Bindery, Camden, N. J.

COLOR BY OVERPRINTING

THE SCIENCE and study of color have many ramifications, but no aspect is more fascinating than the art of printing. Ever since the development of photoengraving, technicians have sought ways of reproducing pictures and designs in richer and more accurate color.

If we have made mistakes, with all our miraculous inventions, perhaps the greatest has been a preoccupation with facsimile reproduction. In an effort to match, down to the most subtle shade, all the color accidents—even the errors—of the artist's brush, color printing has channeled itself into a dead-end alley. Too many printers, engravers and artists have lost sight of the simple fact that what pleases the eye may not necessarily please the soul of a technician, or vice versa.

All the emphasis has been on the point of origin instead of the destination. It is like driving a car with your eyes glued to the mirror instead of on the road ahead. We speak of "originals" in art with a slavish sort of reverence, completely forgetting that, speaking broadly, no one ever sees an artist's "original" except the artist himself and a few people engaged in the reproduction of his painting. Yet thousands or even millions of people may see the printed result.

This adherence to the idea that our aim is to *reproduce* art has tended to remove printing from the field of art entirely. It has had its beneficial effects. We have learned how nearly perfect color facsimiles can be made when necessary. Where we have failed is in forgetting that it is not *always* necessary.

The beginning of our story must concern the artist or designer, since color printing moves according to his genius or his lack of it. The ideal in printing a work of art would be to find some way for the artist to apply printing inks to the paper himself. This, of course, is not practical. But at least the artist can *think* that way. If he ran the press himself, there would be considerable machinery between him and the press sheet. Yet fundamentally, this is no different from using a brush, a pen or a pencil. Between the artist and his paper or canvas there is always a tool of some sort—even if it is his own hand. For the brain to conceive of an artistic work is one thing; to transfer the thought to a surface is another. The process requires tools and physical equipment. The result is always limited by what that equipment can or cannot do.

No honest artist will claim that *his own hand* ever reproduced his thoughts with perfect fidelity. But at least he can train his hand, and he can master the tools he uses until they work for, rather than against him.

Fundamentals of Color Printing

Only by a thorough study of color printing as we know it can the artist make effective use of its existing tools. The tools are extremely versatile. There are many new kinds of plates, new inks, new printing processes being developed constantly. But by and large they are variations, however complex, on basic principles of printing and photography.

Color printing itself may be broken down for our purposes into two categories: full color, or "photomechanical" process reproduction; and solid-color printing from line plates.

It makes no difference whether the printing method to be used is letterpress, offset, gravure or one of the photogelatin processes. The business of producing printed pictures or designs in color follows the same pattern from the artist through the camera to the press plate. Photographically a line plate is still a line plate in all the various processes, and full-color process reproduction is always achieved by a camera-filtered breakdown of the colors into their basic primaries of yellow, red and blue, with a black plate to provide depth and sharpness.

Occasionally, in expensive or exacting jobs of color reproduction, other hues are added to the primaries, but for all practical purposes we can consider that full-color printing is a four-color process.

This fact has resulted in the development of high-speed presses designed to carry two to four inks in a single run. Although there are five- and six-color presses, they are usually not found in any but highly specialized plants.

All these facts are sufficiently well-known to need no elaboration. The only reason they are mentioned at all is that they have a direct bearing upon the planning of this book, and, indeed, upon the artist, publisher or printer who works within the framework of twentieth-century graphic arts.

We are equipped with a marvelous array of tools to spread color over the pages of books and magazines, or on boxes, wrappings and advertising pieces. What shall we do with them?

Naturally, we will go on using them as we have been doing—with improvements as we go along. At the same time, there may be fresh avenues suggested by the machines themselves, which is frequently the way technical innovations come into being. Just as an artist discovered that the lowly palette knife (which artists had always used simply to scrape old paint from their palettes) could be used as an actual painting tool with new effect, so may parts of the accepted printing processes suddenly emerge in a new application.

Color by overprinting is offered as one new approach with startling potentialities.

Actually there is nothing basically new about any of the ideas or information contained in this book. This is simply a realignment of well-known factors both in art and in color printing.

Let us go back to an earlier point by re-examining the full-color process reproduction. Under a magnifying glass, we find that the brown tones are not brown at all, but a kaleidoscopic sprinkling of red, yellow, blue and black dots. That is the way halftone plates and color reproductions are made. But the fact, however ingeniously conceived, is also disillusioning. Not only is our eye being fooled, in a sense, so far as color is concerned, but we are not looking at a halftone at all. What we have come to accept as halftone reproduction, with all its suggestion of soft tonality, is in reality nothing but a solid-color line plate, so finely stippled by mechanical screening that we receive the *impression* of tone. What looks pink on the red plate is in reality a series of bright red marks on the paper, with white spaces in between.

Having reviewed these points, we may establish a syllogism:

1. Printing (except for certain photogelatin processes) is basically a line or solid-color medium.

2. At best, color printing can only approximate and suggest to the eye the effects achieved by an artist with oils, tempera, water colors, pastels, etc.

Therefore, artists who make artwork to be printed should work in *line* (solid colors, separated as are the printing plates themselves).

This, obviously, is an oversimplification. If artists were fanatical or foolish enough to work solely in line, many a beautiful painting would be lost to the world. Furthermore, since we have developed a highly practical way of reproducing halftone and painting effects, it would be ridiculous to discard either the method or the excellent results which can be achieved by it.

What we can do is to study the above proposition and see just how far it may lead us along a new art and color-printing highway.

Color Multiples

A glance at the color-chart pages will show what happens when certain transparent printing inks overlap. Of course, they become "mixed," giving us additional colors. This, too, is a well-known fact and one which has been applied in printing for many years. But no one has taken the trouble to use it to full advantage. Few printers at this writing, and fewer artists, realize that by printing three solid colors, *seven* will appear on the printed surface if they are properly arranged, or that by adding a *fourth* basic color to the overprinted inks, fifteen separate and distinct solid colors may be produced.

Thus it can be seen how completely artists and printers of artwork have been missing a million-dollar bet in the general run of commercial color printing. We can print *seven* colors with three impressions and *fifteen* colors with four impressions, yet we complain because it costs too much to do a job in six colors!

Or, we might spend several hundred dollars on a set of full-color process plates to reproduce some dark, colorless oil painting when we could make plates for a beautiful seven-color line illustration for one-third the cost—or *less!*

This is all very well; still we are faced with problems.

Art directors must find artists who have, or can, master techniques of preparing artwork for effective color overprinting. Artists are often faced with art directors whose limited knowledge of the subject keeps them fearful of making the plunge into new techniques. And both are faced with engravers and printers who suffer the same timidity.

In spite of these factors, more and more examples of color overprinting are appearing. Certain nationally distributed periodicals have used the principle with great success for some time. A few book publishers have taken definite steps to employ color overprinting for jackets and text illustrations. Nevertheless, nowhere has the principle been crystallized into a clear-cut set of standards on which a new art can be based. Nor has the method become widespread enough to be common knowledge throughout the graphic arts industry.

After reading this, some may wonder why such a simple principle should have been so vastly neglected all these years. Like most innovations, the answer may lie partly in its very simplicity. The human mind, in its complexity, tends to search out the answers to infinite problems while some of the most obvious things lie close at hand, unnoticed. This may be part of the answer.

Tools for Overprinted Art

Another part of the answer lies in the need for three essential tools to do the job properly.

The first of these tools belongs to the artist exclusively—his ingenuity, talent, imagination, or whatever you choose to call it. The beauty and quality of his drawings depend *not* on whether he uses full color, but on how skilfully he uses the color at his command, no matter how limited the palette may be.

The second tool is also for the artist. It was developed comparatively recently—oddly enough for a different purpose initially than for color overprinting. This tool consists of color-coated sheets of acetate which, like transparent inks, result in multiple color combinations when placed one over the other. By using a stylus or other sharpened instrument, the color can easily be removed by the artist in those areas where it is not wanted. Thus, instead of building his color on a white surface, from light to dark, he works in reverse, from dark to light.

These transparent Bourges color sheets are a patented commercial product now available in most art supply stores. They are used for many different purposes in commercial art, the primary one being, originally, to provide an inexpensive substitute for full-color process, and much of this preseparated art is reproduced in halftone plates. But the very nature of the color on these sheets, being solid tints, suggests the application of ink to paper in exactly the same manner, with, of course, the same result.

Line cuts over *line cuts*. Transparent color over transparent color to produce secondary hues where they overlap. This is the essence of color by overprinting.

Even with these tools available to us, one more is sorely needed to give artists, art directors, engravers and printers full control over the process. It is a tool to make science out of guesswork. It is a piece of equipment which should have innumerable uses and applications. It is a yardstick by which everyone who is concerned with color printing in any form may set his sights.

The final tool to open the gates into a broad new highway of color printing is this book.

It is by no means claimed that COLOR BY OVERPRINTING is either the first or the last word on the subject. On the contrary, its aim is to furnish a strong foundation on which innumerable new ideas—even new books on and by this method—may be built.

The book, as well as the method itself, is limited by economic considerations. But an effort has been made to select and diagram a highly complex range of possibilities in the simplest possible form.

Why Eleven Basic Colors?

It has been seen how the arithmetical progression of groupings multiplies with the addition of each new color. Obviously, anything but a carefully limited list of basic tints would produce infinite multiples beyond any practical presentation. The basic colors for this text number eleven.

The selection has not been arbitrarily made. There is a definite reason for each basic color being on the list. For example, no color groupings would be adequate without the full spectrum being represented. This consists of six colors: red, orange, yellow, green, blue, purple. So far so good. But this group alone would not be adequate for a comprehensive coverage of the subject. There is also the problem of which red, which blue, etc., will be best for an all-purpose color study.

First, the so-called "process" colors were selected for the list. These are the time-tested basic yellow, red and blue used in full-color reproduction. Experience has proved them to be the best to produce the secondary colors—orange, green and purple. However, for overprinting, medium tints of the process colors have been chosen for greater brilliance and transparency.

Next, since all the process colors tend toward coolness, a warmer group of primaries is added. These are the chrome yellow, red, and royal blue.

For the orange, green and purple we have selected intermediate shades of what might be called as nearly "true" colors as possible.

Finally we have the two neutrals, brown and gray, to provide a wide variety of subtle shades when they are combined with the spectrum colors. The gray may be achieved by using a 50% screen of black, or by using the gray ink specified by number. The advantage of using a screen of black is obvious, as most printing requires black for text matter. Thus, an effect of four overlapping colors plus black can be obtained by using any four-color group containing gray, though only three colors plus black are required in the printing.

The Color Charts

Beginning on page 19 are presented 165 tricolor groups made up from our basic list of eleven colors. These represent all the possible combinations. Some of these may have little practical application. Such combinations as chrome yellow, process yellow, and orange offer negligible contrast. Each of these colors is so similar that most of the overprinted areas are scarcely distinguishable, one from another.

Nevertheless, for the sake of complete coverage of the subject, even such combinations will be found among the tricolor and quadruple groupings. The latter appear in eight rectangles beneath each tricolor group. These color blocks show the colors resulting when each of the remaining eight basic colors is added to the tricolor group.

The reason for showing three- and four-color groupings of the colors should be fairly obvious. Since the general run of multicolor printing uses a maximum of four impressions, we have provided examples to cover the vast majority of printing requirements. For printing in three colors, plus black, the tricolor groupings may be used as the guide. And, of course, the four-color groups show the complete range of quadruple overprinting combinations, 330 in all.

Where only two colors are to be used, any overprinted combination of two of the eleven basic inks can be found within the three- and four-color groups.

It will be noticed that every four-color group is repeated four times throughout the book. This is due to the fact that within each four-color grouping there are four possible groupings of three colors. Since each of these tricolor combinations appears on a separate page, a duplicate four-color group is also shown on each of the four pages involved.

The arrangement of tricolor groups starts with the warmer combinations, proceeds through more balanced groups, then to the cool families. This classification has been made to simplify locating of a particular group.

One more thing requires comment. Although this book is designed primarily as a tool for those engaged in graphic arts, illustrations produced by color overprinting have been selected with the hope that they will excite the imaginations of artists and printers of art. If these examples suggest what may be done to develop a new art as well as a new technique of printing; if they stir the ingenuity of creative artists and artisans, then this book will have served its greatest purpose—to take the first big step on a new and little-known artistic trail.

ART PREPARATION FOR OVERPRINTING

Registration of Transparent Overlays

SINCE the principle of applying overprinted inks depends upon the furnishing of preseparated art copy, it is necessary for artists to learn the best techniques of making color overlays. Each color is printed separately. Working backward from the press plates, it follows that each color must be photographed separately and, in turn, each color must be prepared separately by the artist. The greatest single problem, mechanically, is the maintenance of perfect register throughout the various steps involved.

In the case of full-color painting, one set of register marks will suffice, since the same piece of artwork is before the camera each time a color separation negative is made. But if several overlays must be photographed individually, it follows that identical register marks must appear on each overlay, and that any variation or imperfection in the placement of these marks may throw the whole picture out of register by the time it reaches the printing press.

To overcome this difficulty, the following procedure is recommended in the preparation of any form of transparent or translucent overlays.

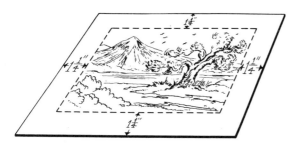

1. First, obtain a piece of good grade white illustration board on which to make the India ink key drawing or pencil guide. This board should have ample margins, beyond the picture area, to provide space for mounting overlays and ruling register marks.

As shown above, the margins should measure at least 1¼″ all around for best results.

2. In India ink, rule center marks ⅛″ from the picture area. All marks should be as sharp and as finely drawn as possible.

3. Now draw corner marks, extended from each border of the picture area.

It is important to rule the register marks carefully and center them accurately.

4. The drawing is now ready for overlays to be taped in position. The overlay sheets themselves should be cut to extend just beyond the corner marks. An overhang of $1/_{16}$″ is sufficient, except on the taped edge, which must have enough overhang beyond the register marks to keep the tape away from them.

Half-inch masking tape or cellulose tape may be used. Place overlay #1 in position, with the tape at top edge.

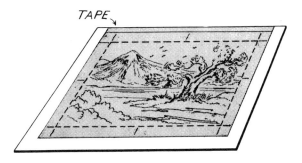

TAPE

5. Next, place overlay #2 in position, taping it along the left-hand edge.

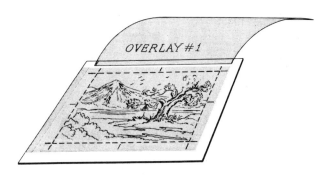

OVERLAY #1

6. Place overlay #3 in position, taping it along the right-hand edge. If four overlays are used, tape the fourth overlay sheet along the bottom edge. Now, with four color sheets in position, the art copy is ready for work.

It will be seen that the overlays, when arranged in this manner, can be flapped into any relationship or arrangement desired. This is especially important when Bourges sheets are being used. Any sheet may be placed on the top, on the bottom, or in second or third position. Any combination of the four overlays can be seen by a quick rearrangement, such as 1 plus 2, 2 plus 3, 1 plus 2 plus 4, 2 plus 3 plus 4, etc.

Because the order in which the colors are printed affects the overprinted hues slightly, it is best in the placement of overlays to follow a standard rule which will indicate to the engraver and printer in what order you wish the inks to be laid down. The above arrangement is suggested as a good standard to be used by everyone concerned. Knowing this rule, the printer would run the color whose overlay is taped at the top *first*, the one taped at the left *second*, and so on, regardless of which overlay happened to be next to the illustration board when the artwork came into his hands.

In general, the best rule is to start with the lightest, brightest color next to the paper and proceed to the darkest, either in arranging the overlays for best effect or in applying inks in the printing process.

However, it should be noted that the ink first applied to the paper will have the maximum effect on the finished printed picture. In other

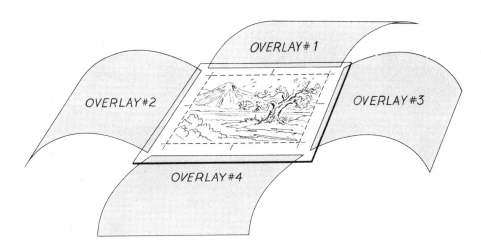

OVERLAY #1

OVERLAY #2

OVERLAY #3

OVERLAY #4

words, if yellow is the first color printed, the entire picture will tend to take on a warm cast, whereas if blue is printed first, a bluish cast may result.

This is the reverse of what many people seem to expect, as the first inclination is to assume that the last color printed should tend to cover up the others. In transparent inks, however, the under colors glow through the overprinted shades, having the same effect as though the second or third colors were printed on a tinted, instead of on a white paper.

In this connection it should be remembered that if any but a nearly pure white paper is to be used in color overprinting, the artist should work transparent color overlays over a paper identical to the stock for the job. Otherwise the resulting printed colors will be quite different from those achieved on the artwork.

It is a good plan, if possible, for the artist to slide a sheet of the proposed printing stock under Bourges or any other transparent overlay art in any case, to see exactly what effect, if any, the paper will have on the reproduction of his picture.

7. We now come to the artist's final step in preparing his artwork for perfect register. If Bourges sheets are being used, excess color should be removed from each overlay sheet to permit all register marks to show through. This may be done by means of "windows," or if time permits and neatness is desired, the en-

tire border may be clear. The picture itself may be separated from the excess border color by no more than ⅛″ to ¼″ of white, in order to save time and unnecessary work.

Using a needle point tool, or the point of a compass, sharply score the acetate of each overlay to provide corner and center marks corresponding with those on the board. Cover these cuts in the acetate with a generous application of black lithograph crayon, then wipe the surface clean with a soft cloth, leaving a deposit of black in the scored lines. This provides fine, sharp register marks, ready for the camera.

Working on Bourges Sheets

Bourges sheets as an art medium are still too new for a thorough coverage of techniques and methods of working them. Each artist must do his own experimenting and find his own style, as he must with any medium. There are, however, certain tools available for removing the color from the acetate, and each produces individual effects for line reproduction. Plastic and wooden styluses are part of the standard Bourges equipment. They can be used for fine detail (using the pointed end) or broad strokes (using the flat blade end).

Other implements which have been used successfully on Bourges material include metal scratchboard or woodcut tools, razors, sandpaper, steel wool, and mimeograph styluses. Sharply pointed metal tools must be used with a light touch or they will cut through the acetate or leave deeply scored lines which may register as shadows in reproduction. Large areas of the color are easily and quickly removed by a cloth dampened with Bourges color remover.

If the artist makes a mistake, and removes color where he wants it retained, he may correct the error by filling in with India ink or with Bourges liquid in a color matching the sheet being worked. India ink should be used only when the reproduction is to be in line. Although such corrections show up as ugly black spots on the artwork, they have no effect on the line negative or press plate, since all color registers as a solid printing area.

For this reason it is very easy to combine type or lettering with Bourges overlay line art. Reproduction proofs, photostatic negatives or positives of type can be attached directly to the Bourges overlay with rubber cement. Although these photostats show as black and white on the artwork, they will, of course, print in whatever color ink is applied to the ultimate press plate.

The basic outline of any Bourges drawing may be worked out in pencil on the illustration board to which the overlay sheets will be attached. Better still, the drawing may be done on a piece of tracing paper, taped securely to the board. The tracing sheet may then be removed when the work on overlays is complete, leaving a clean, unmarked board as a background for the Bourges art.

When the engraver receives artwork which has been prepared as described earlier, he has a complete set of guides for registration. When photographing by reflected light, the camera work may be done *without* removing the overlays from the board. By the simple device of cutting a rectangle of opaque white paper, or lightweight card, the engraver can block out all but the top overlay. In this way all the overlays can be photographed without disturbing their original positions.

Transparent overlays must be removed from the board if they are to be photographed by transmitted light, or light *passing through* the sheets themselves. This direct contact method of making film negatives or deep-etch offset plates produces sharp detail, and will probably point the way to new developments in the reproduction of overprinted art. All "same size"

Bourges art in this book was photographed by transmitted light.

Consultation between artist and printer, or engraver, is always helpful, and should be held whenever possible. In such cases, the parties involved may develop their own methods or special techniques which are better adapted to the specific problem than any general rule set forth in a book of this kind.

Other Methods of Preparing Solid-Color Separations

Although many of the overprints in this book were rendered by means of Bourges sheets, some artists prefer to work in other media. No artist should limit himself to a single method of preparing separations, as there are definite advantages, techniques and textures peculiar to each system.

Many interesting examples of overprinting appear regularly in *The Reader's Digest*, whose remarkable art program has been designed around solid-color printing since 1948, at almost the same time that the John C. Winston Company began its own program of overprinting for books. Virtually all the color artwork of the magazine is done in black, without extensive use of the overprinting principle. (See pages 89 and 90 and insert facing page 90.) This merely serves to indicate that considerable exploration in this field is desirable. New overlay materials are needed, similar to Bourges, but with a wider range of colors suitable for book work or for tastes which run to greater subtlety of color. Transparent color sheets with textured surfaces would add a great deal to the flexibility of the medium. And finally, a good set of colors in transparent fluid or waxy substance which could be used to build compositions on a *clear* surface, instead of the reverse, would make it possible to draw in the conventional manner and still have a visual overlapping of the colors employed.

These things will come. In the meantime, artists who wish to work in black on a white surface have a number of possibilities open to them. Using this book as a guide to what will happen when certain colors overprint, the artist can begin his key drawing on regular illustration board. Subsequent overlays or "mechanicals" of heavy tracing paper, Traceoline, frosted acetate, tracing cloth or any other suitable translucent material can be rendered over the key. The color areas are painted or drawn on the overlays in India ink.

Another method is to execute the drawings for all colors over a light-table, using comparatively thin papers, such as charcoal or light-weight water-color paper. So long as the paper is thin enough for the light to shine through at least two layers, each color can be registered over a key in the same manner as with transparent overlays.

One of the oldest, yet most successful, methods is to make a line plate of the key drawing before color separation is started. This plate is proofed on illustration board in pale, nonphoto blue ink, and subsequent color separations are inked in over the blue impressions. In offset lithography, these blue "keys" can be furnished in any desired size—either larger, same size, or smaller than the ultimate print—on acetate or drawing board. When photographed in the plate-making operation, the pale blue drops out and only the black areas are retained. Artwork for the color charts in this book was prepared by the blue proof method.

The difficulty with all black and white treatment of color separation is that of visualizing the finished color effect. For this reason, the transparent color overlay will inevitably be the answer for most artists of the future. The fact that completely satisfactory materials have yet to be developed is due primarily to the fact that few people have recognized the need for them.

Color Variations

Lacking a range of softer, more subtle basic colors, we have run *The Reader's Digest* illustrations separately, matching their original colors as closely as possible. Some of these colors could be classed as lighter, grayer hues of the basic eleven inks. Not only does this show an interesting comparison, and how line plates can be used in different combinations of color, but it offers some basis for estimating the result of softening the standard colors established here. In other words, an artist may work in the Bourges Process Yellow, Poster Red and Purple. But in his instruction to the printer, if he desires a more subtle effect, he can include color swatches of an ocher, grayed pink, and lavender-gray to correspond with his three overlays.

Thus it is important to bear in mind that the basic eleven inks in COLOR BY OVERPRINTING represent the standard from which innumerable variations can be made. And the color charts themselves can serve as a guide for subdued shades of the same basic colors. It follows that if lemon yellow is changed to an ocher, and bright blue is changed to gray-blue, their overprinted secondary color will be a moss green, rather than the bright green overprint of the original inks. The same principle applies to the *value* or *strength* of the inks used: lighter inks producing lighter overprints, darker inks resulting in darker overprints. To a limited extent, particularly in offset printing, the strength of the inks can be controlled on press while the job is actually being run, by adding thinner, and by increasing or decreasing the flow of ink from the fountain.

In all cases, the secondary and tertiary overprinted colors will follow the same general pattern, provided the primaries are variations of the same basic colors.

Paper as the First Color

The color charts in this book can be used in some degree to determine the effect of certain transparent inks when printed on a tinted stock. If one of the pure, base colors represents the paper, each impression of transparent ink will result in colors similar to the overprints of other inks in the same diagram. For example, if canary yellow paper is to be used, any four-color group containing process yellow will serve as a guide. A transparent blue ink will produce green when printed on the yellow stock; magenta will produce an orange red, and so forth.

In determining the overprinted colors on a tinted paper, it must be remembered that all colors are automatically one step removed from white. The first ink to be applied immediately produces a secondary color. When a second ink overprints the first, the resulting color will be a combination of three: the tint of the paper plus two inks. At the same time the pure colors of the inks themselves, as they appear on a white surface, must be eliminated from any design so printed, and the maximum number of colors to be achieved with three inks is eight—the seven produced by tricolor overprinting, plus the color

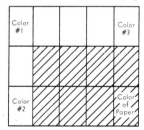

of the paper itself. These eight colors would be represented in the color charts by the eight small rectangles in the lower right of each four-color group.

Looking Forward

It is clear that a new art form is developing —an art form based upon a concept of the printing press as an artist's tool, printer's ink as an art medium. What it requires, in order to become universal, is new equipment for artists, made to the artists' specifications but designed to fit the requirements of modern printing. It is a curious thing to observe the phenomenal strides being made constantly in the printing industry while artists still struggle to make preseparated art by the same crude methods of former times. The painstaking efforts to achieve color effects with India ink drawings on separate pieces of board are not only old-fashioned but cannot possibly make full use of the overprinting principle. Regardless of how skilful artists may become in the translation of color to black and white separations, they can never be completely happy with a method so far removed from the finished effect. Clients, too, generally prefer to see visual art copy.

During great art eras of the past, artists ground their own colors, prepared their own surfaces, invented new tools or techniques to fit the art problems of the time. Today the artist's ingenuity, as well as his talent, must be brought to bear once more. Although he is not likely to make new tools himself, he can tell manufacturers of art supplies what he needs. For color separation work, and particularly for the making of overprints, he needs a new type of transparent color which can be applied to a transparent surface and he needs new applicators which can achieve fine lines or rough texture on such overlays. Just what form these tools may take, we cannot say. But as soon as the printing and art worlds realize what magnificent pictorial art awaits their development, a whole new array of overprint tools will be in constant demand.

INKS FOR COLOR BY OVERPRINTING

Transparent Oil Base Inks

THE SELECTED ELEVEN basic transparent colors shown in this book, and which are arranged in hundreds of overprinted combinations, provide a dictionary of color, the brilliance of which the halftone process could scarcely duplicate.

Of course, the potential range of colors available to the buyer of printing is almost limitless. So many variations of the basic eleven inks are possible that no one could tabulate them all. Nevertheless, in order to set up a standard, these shades were chosen with extreme care, both in respect to color and to strength.

Each color is available in either regular or gloss ink and can be applied to most white coated and uncoated stocks by letterpress or offset.

In the formulation of transparent inks, the inkmaker is allowed a wide latitude. Colors in this book can be considerably increased in strength, allowing the printer to carry less ink on his form whenever, for some reason, he must do so. They will also stand for reduction in color intensity, permitting the printer to increase the ink flow without too much change in the overprint color.

On multicolor work, using either a single- or two-color press, consideration should be given to an opaque first-down color, since the physical characteristics of opaque ink lend to better trapping of the transparent overprint colors. This applies when a job is run single-color press with first-down color dry before the transparent overprint is put on; or with a two-color wet printing operation. A properly applied first-down color, whether run wet or dry, provides the necessary foundation for the subsequent overprinting of transparent inks from solid line plates.

When overprinting with transparent inks, whether by offset or letterpress, a semigloss finish should be expected to occur in the overprint color. In certain cases, dullness in the overprint can be built into the second color, if desired, but the ink manufacturer should be apprised of the client's preference.

In letterpress, heavy solid overprinting past the third impression may cause serious difficulty. The amount of ink necessarily carried for good coverage usually will not permit the laying of four heavy solid impressions, one on top of another, with any degree of success. Nevertheless, a way may yet be found to solve the problem, particularly if there is enough demand for a solution. Most ink developments have taken place after a specific need has been established, and there is no reason to assume an exception in this case.

This problem is not as prevalent in the offset process, which transmits a finer ink film.

Should the end use of the printed piece indicate that certain characteristics must be built into the ink, such as soap-proofness, grease-proofness, alcohol resistance, extreme permanency, etc., the inkmaker must be aware of these requirements, since unusual specifications will limit the pigments he may safely use and might even make impossible a good color match.

To benefit fully from the inkmaker's experience with transparent inks, the printer should advise him of all factors involved: the type of press (single- or multi-color); the art copy (size of solid areas and the amount of overprint); the expected lapse of time between overprint colors; the paper stock; and the intended end use of the job. The inkmaker should know if the print must withstand severe scuffing, if it will be overprinted with varnish or run with a gloss ink.

With such information at the ink manufacturer's disposal, the printer and his client can be assured of proper inks for the job.

Overprinting by Flexography

OF THE FOUR main classes of printing, flexography is the one most ideally suited to overprinting, since at least 95% of flexographic work is done with line plates. To understand the reason for the relative absence of screened or halftone reproduction in this field, a brief review of the process should be made.

Flexography is a rotary letterpress operation in which rubber plates are used to print a moving web of plastic or paper with inks which dry instantly by evaporation. As originally conceived in Europe in the 1920's, the process was a mechanical rubber stamping operation designed to eliminate large amounts of hand stamping by using inexpensive equipment. As such, the machine was limited to one fountain roller, one form or metering roller, a plate cylinder, on which rubber plates were mounted by cement, and an impression cylinder. To provide instantaneous drying and adequate distribution with only one form or metering roller, inks were made in a fluid form. Colors were obtained by dissolving dyes in alcohol with shellac serving as the resinous binder. This solvent was selected because of economy, ability to dissolve dyes, speed of evaporation and its nonswelling effect on rubber rollers and plates.

Flexography grew from this humble beginning to its present stature because the packaging industry presented problems which could not be solved by conventional letterpress or offset techniques. The use of pigmented flexographic inks on improved presses resulted in odorless, grease-, fat-, and paraffin-resistant prints which could be produced at high speed

and adhere extremely well to cellophane, glassine, papers, parchment and foil. Since these problems have plagued oil printers for some time, flexography became the standard process —along with gravure, which requires longer runs to be economical—for packaging work.

The phenomenal growth of the packaging industry, along with the introduction or expanded use of cellulose acetate, polystyrene, Mylar, Pliofilm and polyethylene, has resulted in establishing flexography as a member of the big four in printing. As pointed out before, the process generally uses line plates because the present limited metering and distribution system requires the use of fluid inks in conjunction with rubber plates. Mobility of the ink, together with the slight deformation of the plate at each inking and printing impression, tends to limit the use of halftone screens. Anything finer than 85-line screens usually requires excessive attention to prevent fill-in, although improvements being made in plates, inks and presses make the future appear much brighter.

Nevertheless, line plates will probably continue to dominate the process for some years and, therefore, color by overprinting is directly applicable to present-day flexographic practices. Furthermore, flexographic inks are available in a complete range from transparent to opaque. Since most flexographic presses are limited to four colors, the press range of the hues can be expanded from four to fifteen with striking effects on gift wraps, foil, glassine, cellophane, Pliofilm, cellulose acetate and polyethylene bags.

All this is achievable without a single process change. It simply requires the use of principles outlined in this book. Co-operation between artist, converter and ink manufacturer is the only requirement for color by overprinting to become standard procedure in the flexographic industry.

Index to Color Groups . . . . The Basic Eleven Inks Plus Black

RED

Index: 0
Corresponding Bourges Color . . . .
   70% Poster Red
No. 11 filter; orthochromatic film

INK NUMBERS

Letterpress:	OP-0
Offset:	OPO-0
Gravure:	OPG-0
Flexographic:	OPF-0

CHROME YELLOW

Index: 1
Corresponding Bourges Color . . . .
   70% Poster Yellow
No. 30 filter; orthochromatic film

INK NUMBERS

Letterpress:	OP-1
Offset:	OPO-1
Gravure:	OPG-1
Flexographic:	OPF-1

PROCESS or LEMON YELLOW*

Index: 2
Corresponding Bourges Color . . . .
   70% Process Yellow
No. 30 filter; orthochromatic film

* If standard Process Yellow is required in printing, this tint may be approximated by a 70% benday screen.

INK NUMBERS

Letterpress:	OP-2
Offset:	OPO-2
Gravure:	OPG-2
Flexographic:	OPF-2

ORANGE

Index: 4
Corresponding Bourges Color . . . .
   100% Orange
No. 30 or No. 47 filter; ortho. film

INK NUMBERS

Letterpress:	OP-4
Offset:	OPO-4
Gravure:	OPG-4
Flexographic:	OPF-4

PROCESS RED or MAGENTA*

Index: 6
Corresponding Bourges Color . . . .
   70% Process Red
No. 11 filter; orthochromatic film

INK NUMBERS

Letterpress:	OP-6
Offset:	OPO-6
Gravure:	OPG-6
Flexographic:	OPF-6

* If standard Process Red is required in printing, this tint may be approximated by a 70% benday screen.

BROWN

Index: 12
Corresponding Bourges Color . . . .
   50% Brown
No. 47 filter; orthochromatic film.

INK NUMBERS

Letterpress:	OP-12
Offset:	OPO-12
Gravure:	OPG-12
Flexographic:	OPF-12

Manufacturer: Bensing Brothers and Deeney Sales Company, Philadelphia.

GRAY (or 50% benday screen of Black)

Index: 17
Corresponding Bourges Color . . . .
50% Black
Underexpose; overdevelop.

INK NUMBERS

Letterpress:	OP-17
Offset:	OPO-17
Gravure:	OPG-17
Flexographic:	OPF-17

GREEN

Index: 18
Corresponding Bourges Color . . . .
70% Green
No. 30 filter; orthochromatic film.
No. 29 filter; panchromatic film.

INK NUMBERS

Letterpress:	OP-18
Offset:	OPO-18
Gravure:	OPG-18
Flexographic:	OPF-18

PURPLE

Index: 20
Corresponding Bourges Color . . . .
70% Purple
No. 15 filter; orthochromatic film.

INK NUMBERS

Letterpress:	OP-20
Offset:	OPO-20
Gravure:	OPG-20
Flexographic:	OPF-20

ROYAL BLUE

Index: 32
Corresponding Bourges Color . . . .
70% Poster Blue
No. 12 filter; orthochromatic film.

INK NUMBERS

Letterpress:	OP-32
Offset:	OPO-32
Gravure:	OPG-32
Flexographic:	OPF-32

PROCESS BLUE*

Index: 34
Corresponding Bourges Color . . . .
50% Process Blue
No. 29 filter; panchromatic film.

INK NUMBERS

Letterpress:	OP-34
Offset:	OPO-34
Gravure:	OPG-34
Flexographic:	OPF-34

* If standard Process Blue is required, this tint may be approximated by a 50% benday screen.

BLACK

Index: 99
Corresponding Bourges Color . . . .
100% Black
No filter.

INK NUMBERS

Letterpress:	OP-99
Offset:	OPO-99
Gravure:	OPG-99
Flexographic:	OPF-99

The Basic Eleven Inks

This book is printed in eleven colors, plus black. Each of the eleven basic inks is shown on the preceding two pages. Under the name of each color is shown an index figure. This figure provides a means of determining a systematic order of overprinted colors.

To locate the page showing any tricolor group of your choice, total the three index figures of the colors selected. The desired group will be found under the resulting index figure, which appears at the top of every color chart page.

Following each tricolor group, the four-color groups are shown, likewise in order of their warmth. This order is established by adding the remaining eight colors in sequence, beginning with the lowest index and ending with the highest.

It should be noted that while the inks have been carefully selected to provide the greatest and most practical range of overlapping colors, each one may be darkened or lightened for special purposes to obtain varied effects. Thus considerable control of the final printed result can be exercised after initial proofs are received and analyzed. Also, an unlimited range of other shades and off-color inks could be used for overprinting with great effectiveness. But for the sake of standardization, the "basic eleven" will serve most purposes.

The colors selected for COLOR BY OVERPRINTING *are based upon the Bourges Palette of Standardized Colors, all of which can be matched in Bourges materials.*

WARM GROUPS

index 3 to 45

Included in this section are all tricolor groups with an index of 45 or less. It will be noticed that with five exceptions these groups are made up of at least two colors on the warm side of the scale, or with an index of 17 or lower. The exceptions are groups 79, 85, 91, 97, 101; in each case the second and third colors are green and purple respectively, whose index figures are just over the intermediate 17 of gray. These colors are balanced by one with an index sufficiently low to keep the group within the "warm" section of the book.

This grouping is purely arbitrary for the sake of easy selection or location of specific combinations and has no basis in scientific analysis of each color's place in the spectrum.

18

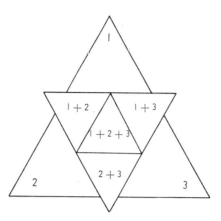

KEY TO TRICOLOR GROUPS

The above diagram shows the seven areas of tricolor overprinting as they appear on the following pages of color guides. Triangles 1, 2 and 3 represent the pure base colors. In the central figure, the overlapping inks are represented by their corresponding numerals. Where color 2 overlaps color 1, the area is designated by the figures 1 + 2, and so forth. All three inks are superimposed in the center triangle, containing the figures 1 + 2 + 3.

1				3
	1 + 3	1+2+3	2 + 3	
1 + 2	1+2+4	1 + 2 +3 + 4	1 + 3 + 4	3 + 4
2	2 + 4	2+3+4	1 + 4	4

KEY TO FOUR-COLOR GROUPS

This diagram provides a key to the fifteen areas of four-color overprinting in the color guides. As in the tricolor figure above, the pure or base colors appear in each corner. Overprinted combinations are designated by numbers indicating the component inks of each block. The center block is always the darkest color, comprising all four inks superimposed. For convenient color chart analysis, these diagrams appear in the lower outside corners of the chart pages.

MATCHING KEY

Base colors: *Index*
  1. red **0**
  2. chrome yellow **1**
  3. process yellow **2**

Inks: **1.**   **2.**   **3.**
  Letterpress — OP-0   OP-1   OP-2
  Offset   — OPO-0   OPO-1   OPO-2
  Gravure   — OPG-0   OPG-1   OPG-2
  Flexographic — OPF-0   OPF-1   OPF-2

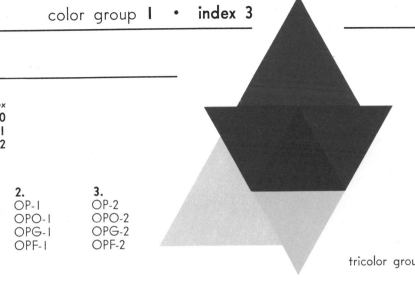

tricolor group 1

A. group 1 plus orange

B. group 1 plus process red

C. group 1 plus brown

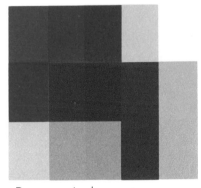

D. group 1 plus gray

E. group 1 plus green

F. group 1 plus purple

G. group 1 plus royal blue

H. group 1 plus process blue

1	1 + 3	1 + 2 + 3	2 + 3	3
1 + 2	1 + 2 + 4	1 + 2 + 3 + 4	1 + 3 + 4	3 + 4
2	2 + 4	2 + 3 + 4	1 + 4	4

four-color key

tricolor group **2**

MATCHING KEY

Base colors: *Index*
1. red **0**
2. chrome yellow **1**
3. orange **4**

Inks: **1.**   **2.**   **3.**

	1.	2.	3.
Letterpress —	OP-0	OP-1	OP-4
Offset —	OPO-0	OPO-1	OPO-4
Gravure —	OPG-0	OPG-1	OPG-4
Flexographic —	OPF-0	OPF-1	OPF-4

A. group 2 plus process yellow

B. group 2 plus process red

C. group 2 plus brown

D. group 2 plus gray

E. group 2 plus green

F. group 2 plus purple

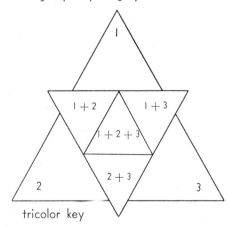

tricolor key

G. group 2 plus royal blue

H. group 2 plus process blue

MATCHING KEY

Base colors: *Index*
     1. red **0**
     2. process yellow **2**
     3. orange **4**

Inks:	**1.**	**2.**	**3.**
Letterpress —	OP-0	OP-2	OP-4
Offset —	OPO-0	OPO-2	OPO-4
Gravure —	OPG-0	OPG-2	OPG-4
Flexographic —	OPF-0	OPF-2	OPF-4

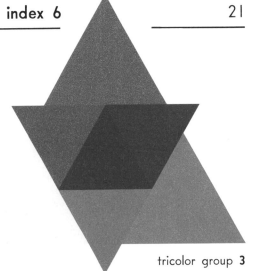

tricolor group **3**

A. group 3 plus chrome yellow

B. group 3 plus process red

C. group 3 plus brown

D. group 3 plus gray

E. group 3 plus green

F. group 3 plus purple

G. group 3 plus royal blue

H. group 3 plus process blue

1	1 + 3	1 + 2 + 3	2 + 3	3
1 + 2	1 + 2 + 4	1 + 2 + 3 + 4	1 + 3 + 4	3 + 4
2	2 + 4	2 + 3 + 4	1 + 4	4

four-color key

TAFFY TROOP

Packaging design by Anna Atene
Color group 3E plus black (also groups 22B, 29B, 39A)
Rendering: Black areas in India ink on illustration board. Color areas on Bourges
        sheets: 70% Poster Yellow, 100% Orange, 70% Poster Red, 70% Green.
        Bourges color remover used in open background areas.
Process: Offset. No reduction.

To no other segment of the graphic arts industry is overprinting so perfectly suited as to packaging. Not only does solid-color overprinting produce the kind of bright, eye-catching designs required by this form of advertising, but because of mechanical limitations line reproduction is already the printing medium most widely used by the packaging industry.

The candy box design opposite is only one of thousands of possible applications. With the development of flexographic inks and the ability to overprint several colors at high speed on such materials as cellophane and foil, the potentialities of overprint techniques are tremendous.

In this particular example, the artist has used overlapping areas of color sparingly. An even greater range of colors could be obtained, if desired, with the same group of inks, as will be seen by referring to color group 3E. However, it should be borne in mind that simply because four inks will produce fifteen solid colors is no reason for feeling obliged to employ all fifteen. On the contrary, the use of color should be determined by the art problem involved and by the artist's taste or feeling for the subject.

tricolor group **4**

MATCHING KEY

Base colors: *Index*
1. red **0**
2. chrome yellow ., ., .,   **1**
3. process red **6**

Inks:	**1.**	**2.**	**3.**
Letterpress —	OP-0	OP-1	OP-6
Offset —	OPO-0	OPO-1	OPO-6
Gravure —	OPG-0	OPG-1	OPG-6
Flexographic —	OPF-0	OPF-1	OPF-6

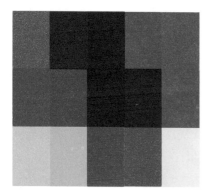

A. group 4 plus process yellow

B. group 4 plus orange

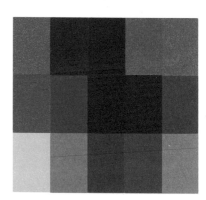

C. group 4 plus brown

D. group 4 plus gray

E. group 4 plus green

F. group 4 plus purple

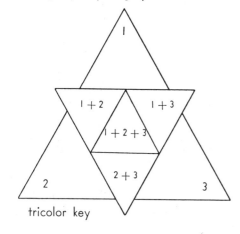

tricolor key

G. group 4 plus royal blue   **H.** group 4 plus process blue

MATCHING KEY

Base colors: *Index*
   1. chrome yellow 1
   2. process yellow 2
   3. orange 4

Inks:	**1.**	**2.**	**3.**
Letterpress —	OP-1	OP-2	OP-4
Offset —	OPO-1	OPO-2	OPO-4
Gravure —	OPG-1	OPG-2	OPG-4
Flexographic —	OPF-1	OPF-2	OPF-4

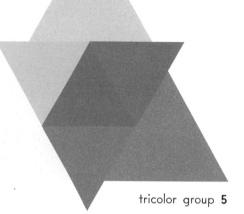

tricolor group **5**

A. group 5 plus red

B. group 5 plus process red

C. group 5 plus brown

D. group 5 plus gray

E. group 5 plus green

F. group 5 plus purple

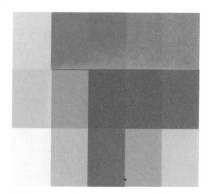

G. group 5 plus royal blue

H. group 5 plus process blue

1	1 + 3	1 + 2 + 3	2 + 3	3
1 + 2	1 + 2 + 4	1 + 2 + 3 + 4	1 + 3 + 4	3 + 4
2	2 + 4	2 + 3 + 4	1 + 4	4

four-color key

tricolor group **6**

MATCHING KEY

Base colors:			*Index*
1. red			0
2. process yellow			?
3. process red			6

Inks:	1.	2.	3.
Letterpress —	OP-0	OP-2	OP-6
Offset —	OPO-0	OPO-2	OPO-6
Gravure —	OPG-0	OPG-2	OPG-6
Flexographic —	OPF-0	OPF-2	OPF-6

A. group 6 plus chrome yellow

B. group 6 plus orange

C. group 6 plus brown

D. group 6 plus gray

E. group 6 plus green

F. group 6 plus purple

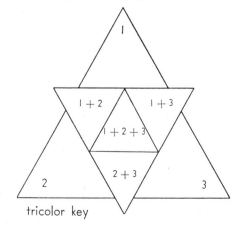

tricolor key

G. group 6 plus royal blue

H. group 6 plus process blue

MATCHING KEY

Base colors: *Index*
1. chrome yellow 1
2. process yellow 2
3. process red 6

Inks: **1.**   **2.**   **3.**

	1.	2.	3.
Letterpress	OP-1	OP-2	OP-6
Offset	OPO-1	OPO-2	OPO-6
Gravure	OPG-1	OPG-2	OPG-6
Flexographic	OPF-1	OPF-2	OPF-6

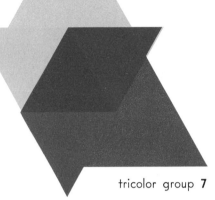

tricolor group **7**

A. group 7 plus red

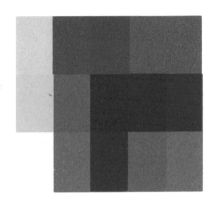

B. group 7 plus orange

C. group 7 plus brown

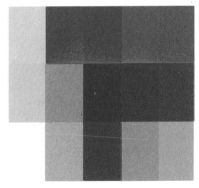

D. group 7 plus gray

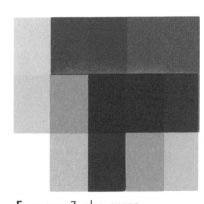

E. group 7 plus green

F. group 7 plus purple

G. group 7 plus royal blue

H. group 7 plus process blue

1	1 + 3	1 + 2 + 3	2 + 3	3
1 + 2	1 + 2 + 4	1 + 2 + 3 + 4	1 + 3 + 4	3 + 4
2	2 + 4	2 + 3 + 4	1 + 4	4

four-color key

tricolor group **8**

MATCHING KEY

Base colors: *Index*
1. red 0
2. orange ......, ... 4
3. process red 6

Inks:	1.	2.	3.
Letterpress	OP-0	OP-4	OP-6
Offset	OPO-0	OPO-4	OPO-6
Gravure	OPG-0	OPG-4	OPG-6
Flexographic	OPF-0	OPF-4	OPF-6

A. group 8 plus chrome yellow

B. group 8 plus process yellow

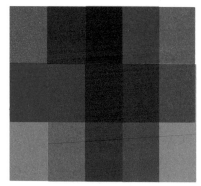

C. group 8 plus brown

D. group 8 plus gray

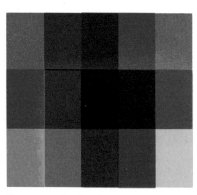

E. group 8 plus green

F. group 8 plus purple

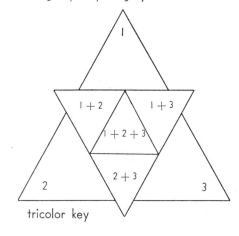

tricolor key

G. group 8 plus royal blue

H. group 8 plus process blue

MATCHING KEY

Base colors:　　　　　*Index*
　　1. chrome yellow . . . .　1
　　2. orange . . . .　4
　　3. process red . . . .　6

Inks:　　　　　**1.**　　　　**2.**　　　　**3.**
　　Letterpress　— OP-1　　OP-4　　OP-6
　　Offset　　　— OPO-1　OPO-4　OPO-6
　　Gravure　　— OPG-1　OPG-4　OPG-6
　　Flexographic — OPF-1　OPF-4　OPF-6

tricolor group **9**

A. group 9 plus red

B. group 9 plus process yellow

C. group 9 plus brown

D. group 9 plus gray

E. group 9 plus green

F. group 9 plus purple

G. group 9 plus royal blue

H. group 9 plus process blue

1	1 + 3	1 + 2 + 3	2 + 3	3
1 + 2	1 + 2 + 4	1 + 2 + 3 + 4	1 + 3 + 4	3 + 4
2	2 + 4	2 + 3 + 4	1 + 4	4

four-color key

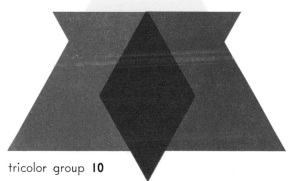

tricolor group 10

MATCHING KEY

Base colors: *Index*
1. process yellow **2**
2. orange **4**
3. process red **6**

Inks:	**1.**	**2.**	**3.**
Letterpress —	OP-2	OP-4	OP-6
Offset —	OPO-2	OPO-4	OPO-6
Gravure —	OPG-2	OPG-4	OPG-6
Flexographic —	OPF-2	OPF-4	OPF-6

A. group 10 plus red

B. group 10 plus chrome yellow

C. group 10 plus brown

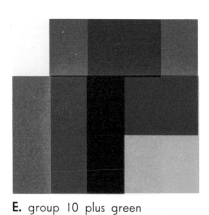

D. group 10 plus gray

E. group 10 plus green

F. group 10 plus purple

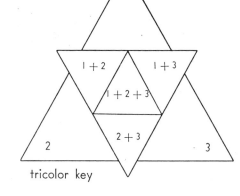

tricolor key

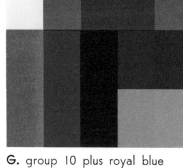

G. group 10 plus royal blue

H. group 10 plus process blue

MATCHING KEY

Base colors: *Index*
    1. red **0**
    2. chrome yellow **1**
    3. brown **12**

Inks:	**1.**	**2.**	**3.**
Letterpress	— OP-0	OP-1	OP-12
Offset	— OPO-0	OPO-1	OPO-12
Gravure	— OPG-0	OPG-1	OPG-12
Flexographic	— OPF-0	OPF-1	OPF-12

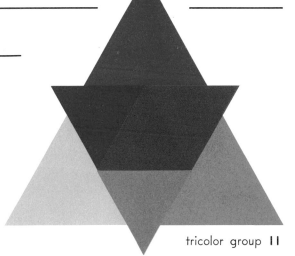

tricolor group 11

A. group 11 plus process yellow

B. group 11 plus orange

C. group 11 plus process red

D. group 11 plus gray

E. group 11 plus green

F. group 11 plus purple

G. group 11 plus royal blue

H. group 11 plus process blue

1	1 + 3	1 + 2 + 3	2 + 3	3
1 + 2	1 + 2 + 4	1 + 2 + 3 + 4	1 + 3 + 4	3 + 4
2	2 + 4	2 + 3 + 4	1 + 4	4

four-color key

tricolor group **12**

MATCHING KEY

Base colors: *Index*
1. red **0**
2. process yellow **2**
3. brown **12**

Inks:	1.	2.	3.
Letterpress —	OP-0	OP-2	OP-12
Offset —	OPO-0	OPO-2	OPO-12
Gravure —	OPG-0	OPG-2	OPG-12
Flexographic —	OPF-0	OPF-2	OPF-12

A. group 12 plus chrome yellow

B. group 12 plus orange

C. group 12 plus process red

D. group 12 plus gray

E. group 12 plus green

F. group 12 plus purple

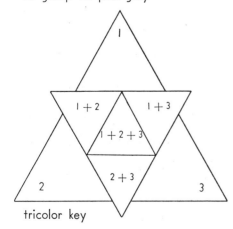

tricolor key

(tricolor key diagram: 1, 1 + 2, 1 + 3, 1 + 2 + 3, 2, 2 + 3, 3)

G. group 12 plus royal blue

H. group 12 plus process blue

MATCHING KEY

Base colors: *Index*
1. chrome yellow 1
2. process yellow 2
3. brown 12

Inks:

	1.	2.	3.
Letterpress	— OP-1	OP-2	OP-12
Offset	— OPO-1	OPO-2	OPO-12
Gravure	— OPG-1	OPG-2	OPG-12
Flexographic	— OPF-1	OPF-2	OPF-12

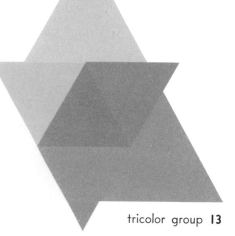

tricolor group **13**

A. group 13 plus red

B. group 13 plus orange

C. group 13 plus process red

D. group 13 plus gray

E. group 13 plus green

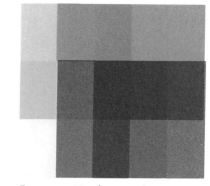

F. group 13 plus purple

G. group 13 plus royal blue

H. group 13 plus process blue

1	1 + 3	1 + 2 + 3	2 + 3	3
1 + 2	1 + 2 + 4	1 + 2 + 3 + 4	1 + 3 + 4	3 + 4
2	2 + 4	2 + 3 + 4	1 + 4	4

four-color key

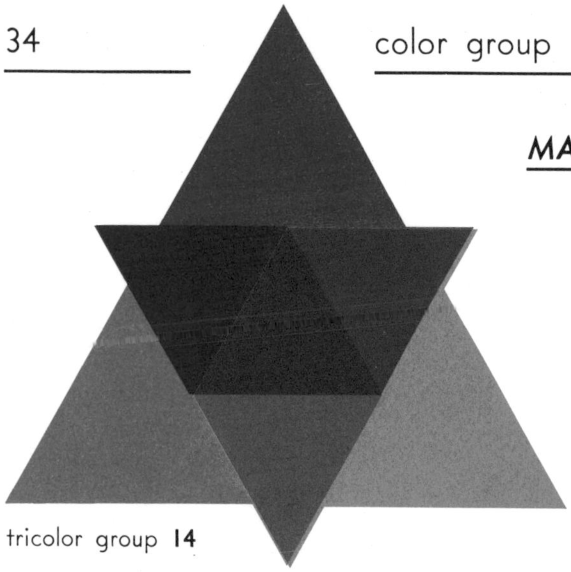

tricolor group **14**

MATCHING KEY

Base colors: *Index*
1. red 0
2. orange 4
3. brown 12

Inks:

	1.	2.	3.
Letterpress —	OP-0	OP-4	OP-12
Offset —	OPO-0	OPO-4	OPO-12
Gravure —	OPG-0	OPG-4	OPG-12
Flexographic —	OPF-0	OPF-4	OPF-12

A. group 14 plus chrome yellow

B. group 14 plus process yellow

C. group 14 plus process red

D. group 14 plus gray

E. group 14 plus green

F. group 14 plus purple

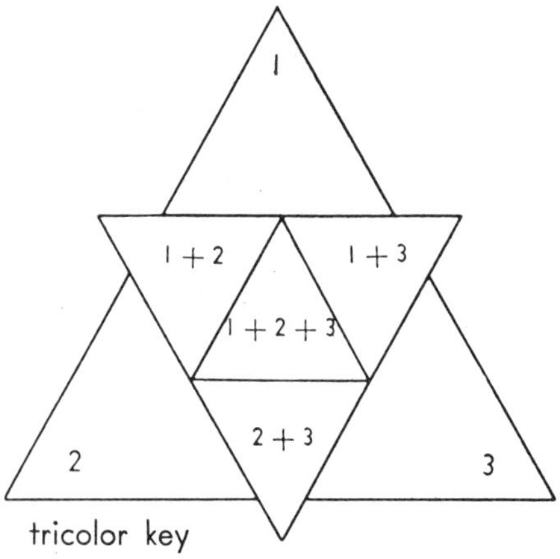

tricolor key

G. group 14 plus royal blue

H. group 14 plus process blue

MATCHING KEY

Base colors: *Index*
1. chrome yellow   1
2. orange   4
3. brown 12

Inks: **1.**   **2.**   **3.**

	1.	2.	3.
Letterpress	— OP-1	OP-4	OP-12
Offset	— OPO-1	OPO-4	OPO-12
Gravure	— OPG-1	OPG-4	OPG-12
Flexographic	— OPF-1	OPF-4	OPF-12

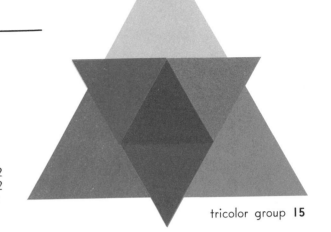

tricolor group **15**

A. group 15 plus red

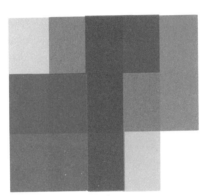

B. group 15 plus process yellow

C. group 15 plus process red

D. group 15 plus gray

E. group 15 plus green

F. group 15 plus purple

G. group 15 plus royal blue

H. group 15 plus process blue

1	1 + 3	1 + 2 + 3	2 + 3	3
1 + 2	1 + 2 + 4	1 + 2 + 3 + 4	1 + 3 + 4	3 + 4
2	2 + 4	2 + 3 + 4	1 + 4	4

four-color key

ROBINSON CRUSOE

Book illustrations by Lyle Justis
Tricolor group 16 plus black
Rendering: Black key, pen and ink on rough-textured paper. Color areas, plastic
stylus on Bourges sheets: 70% Process Yellow, 70% Process Red, 50%
Process Blue.
Process: Offset. No reduction.

Lyle Justis is one of the finest pen and ink draftsmen of all time. He draws as though it were a form of writing, rarely using a pencil guide, but setting down his pictorial ideas exactly as they flow from his pen. Only a great draftsman would dare to draw so directly in India ink, since any errors are permanently recorded and cannot be erased.

In their original reproduction, these overprints were made in the process yellow, red, and blue, matching the Bourges overlays listed above. But in order to demonstrate a color variation, and as a contrast to the process color reproductions of the *Alice* drawings on pages 152 and 153, gray has been substituted for the process blue, and the process yellow and red have been modified to chrome yellow and warm red. The overall result is warmer and at the same time more restrained, yet both color schemes are suitable for the tropical subject.

For another modification of the standard "process" color scheme, see the *Heidi* illustrations on page 86, where a complete new set of inks has been substituted for the process colors. These three sets of illustrations—from *Robinson Crusoe, Alice in Wonderland,* and *Heidi*—are all taken from Winston's PIXIE BOOK editions. It was in this series of condensed classics that multicolor overprinting from Bourges art was first used for the illustration of an entire book. Color overlays in all examples are by Edward F. Cortese.

Illustrations from
the PIXIE BOOK edition of
Robinson Crusoe.
Published by
The John C. Winston Company.

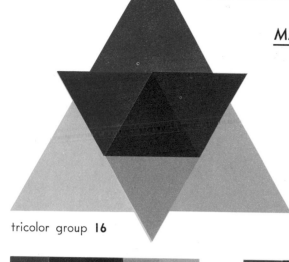

tricolor group **16**

MATCHING KEY

Base colors: *Index*
1. red **0**
2. chrome yellow **1**
3. gray **17**

Inks:		**1.**	**2.**	**3.**
Letterpress	—	OP-0	OP-1	OP-17
Offset	—	OPO-0	OPO-1	OPO-17
Gravure	—	OPG-0	OPG-1	OPG-17
Flexographic	—	OPF-0	OPF-1	OPF-17

A. group 16 plus process yellow

B. group 16 plus orange

C. group 16 plus process red

D. group 16 plus brown

E. group 16 plus green

F. group 16 plus purple

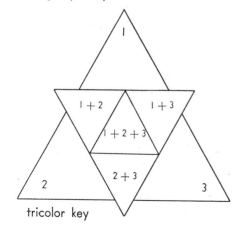

tricolor key

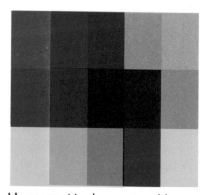

G. group 16 plus royal blue

H. group 16 plus process blue

MATCHING KEY

Base colors: *Index*

     1. red 0
     2. process red 6
     3. brown 12

Inks: **1.**   **2.**   **3.**

	1.	2.	3.
Letterpress —	OP-0	OP-6	OP-12
Offset —	OPO-0	OPO-6	OPO-12
Gravure —	OPG-0	OPG-6	OPG-12
Flexographic —	OPF-0	OPF-6	OPF-12

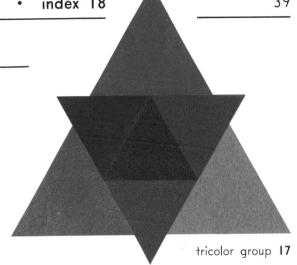

tricolor group **17**

A. group 17 plus chrome yellow

B. group 17 plus process yellow

C. group 17 plus orange

D. group 17 plus gray

E. group 17 plus green

F. group 17 plus purple

G. group 17 plus royal blue

H. group 17 plus process blue

1	1 + 3	1 + 2 + 3	2 + 3	3
1 + 2	1 + 2 + 4	1 + 2 + 3 + 4	1 + 3 + 4	3 + 4
2	2 + 4	2 + 3 + 4	1 + 4	4

four-color key

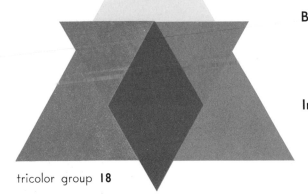

tricolor group **18**

MATCHING KEY

Base colors: *Index*
1. process yellow **2**
2. orange **4**
3. brown **12**

Inks:	1.	2.	3.
Letterpress —	OP-2	OP-4	OP-12
Offset —	OPO-2	OPO-4	OPO-12
Gravure —	OPG-2	OPG-4	OPG-12
Flexographic —	OPF-2	OPF-4	OPF-12

A. group 18 plus red

B. group 18 plus chrome yellow

C. group 18 plus process red

D. group 18 plus gray

E. group 18 plus green

F. group 18 plus purple

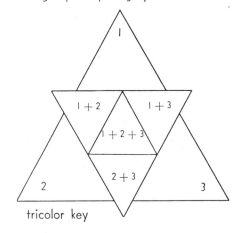

tricolor key

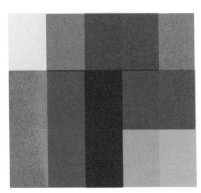

G. group 18 plus royal blue

H. group 18 plus process blue

MATCHING KEY

Base colors: *Index*
   1. red 0
   2. chrome yellow 1
   3. green 18

Inks: **1.**   **2.**   **3.**
  Letterpress — OP-0   OP-1   OP-18
  Offset — OPO-0   OPO-1   OPO-18
  Gravure — OPG-0   OPG-1   OPG-18
  Flexographic — OPF-0   OPF-1   OPF-18

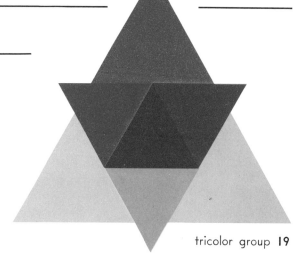

tricolor group **19**

A. group 19 plus process yellow

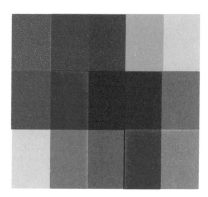

B. group 19 plus orange

C. group 19 plus process red

D. group 19 plus brown

E. group 19 plus gray

F. group 19 plus purple

G. group 19 plus royal blue

H. group 19 plus process blue

four-color key

WOODLAND MEETING

Juvenile book illustration by Donald E. Cooke
Color group 20H plus black (also groups 68E, 116B, 126A)
Rendering: Black areas, India ink on illustration board. Color areas, plastic stylus on Bourges sheets: 70% Process Yellow, 70% Poster Red, 50% Process Blue, 50% Black.
Process: Offset. No reduction.

On these facing pages, the same illustration is shown reproduced in two different ways. Above, the picture is printed in five colors: process yellow, red, process blue, gray, and black. All five plates were made in line from a black drawing and four Bourges overlays of the colors listed above. For many practical printing requirements, the use of five inks would be too costly. But since one of the colors is gray, the same picture can be reduced to four impressions as shown at the right.

WOODLAND MEETING

Tricolor group 68 plus combination benday and line black plate.

Rendering: Black areas, India ink on illustration board. Color areas, plastic stylus on Bourges sheets: 70% Process Yellow, 70% Poster Red, 50% Process Blue, 50% Black.

Process: Offset. No reduction.

Here is the same illustration made for four-color printing. To achieve this result, the cameraman made a silhouette of the gray overlay on acetate film. He then placed a 50% screened tint on the contact side of this negative. With the screened "gray" negative in register with the "black" line image, a single positive, or the plate itself, could be made, containing both the solid black and the gray areas. The printed result is close enough to the five-color reproduction at the left to satisfy artistic taste as well as practical requirements.

tricolor group **20**

MATCHING KEY

Base colors:			*Index*
1. red			**0**
2. process yellow			**2**
3. gray			**17**

Inks:	**1.**	**2.**	**3.**
Letterpress —	OP-0	OP-2	OP-17
Offset —	OPO-0	OPO-2	OPO-17
Gravure —	OPG-0	OPG-2	OPG-17
Flexographic —	OPF-0	OPF-2	OPF-17

A. group 20 plus chrome yellow

B. group 20 plus orange

C. group 20 plus process red

D. group 20 plus brown

E. group 20 plus green

F. group 20 plus purple

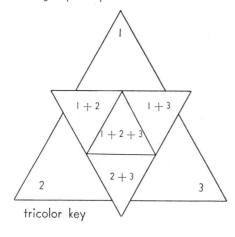

tricolor key

G. group 20 plus royal blue

H. group 20 plus process blue

MATCHING KEY

Base colors: _Index_
1. chrome yellow I
2. process red 6
3. brown 12

Inks:	**1.**	**2.**	**3.**
Letterpress —	OP-1	OP-6	OP-12
Offset —	OPO-1	OPO-6	OPO-12
Gravure —	OPG-1	OPG-6	OPG-12
Flexographic —	OPF-1	OPF-6	OPF-12

tricolor group **21**

A. group 21 plus red

B. group 21 plus process yellow

C. group 21 plus orange

D. group 21 plus gray

E. group 21 plus green

F. group 21 plus purple

G. group 21 plus royal blue

H. group 21 plus process blue

1	1 + 3	1 + 2 + 3	2 + 3	3
1 + 2	1 + 2 + 4	1 + 2 + 3 + 4	1 + 3 + 4	3 + 4
2	2 + 4	2 + 3 + 4	1 + 4	4

four-color key

tricolor group **22**

MATCHING KEY

Base colors:			*Index*
1. red			0
2. process yellow			2
3. green			18

Inks:	**1.**	**2.**	**3.**
Letterpress —	OP-0	OP-2	OP-18
Offset —	OPO-0	OPO-2	OPO-18
Gravure —	OPG-0	OPG-2	OPG-18
Flexographic —	OPF-0	OPF-2	OPF-18

A. group 22 plus chrome yellow

B. group 22 plus orange

C. group 22 plus process red

D. group 22 plus brown

E. group 22 plus gray

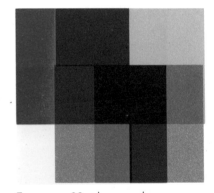

F. group 22 plus purple

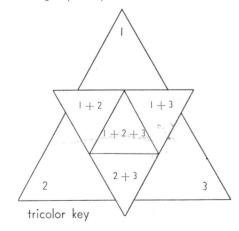

tricolor key

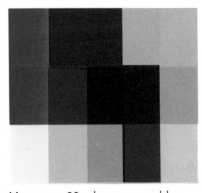

G. group 22 plus royal blue

H. group 22 plus process blue

MATCHING KEY

Base colors: *Index*
- 1. chrome yellow 1
- 2. process yellow 2
- 3. gray 17

Inks:	1.	2.	3.
Letterpress —	OP-1	OP-2	OP-17
Offset —	OPO-1	OPO-2	OPO-17
Gravure —	OPG-1	OPG-2	OPG-17
Flexographic —	OPF-1	OPF-2	OPF-17

tricolor group **23**

A. group 23 plus red

B. group 23 plus orange

C. group 23 plus process red

D. group 23 plus brown

E. group 23 plus green

F. group 23 plus purple

G. group 23 plus royal blue

H. group 23 plus process blue

1	1 + 3	1 + 2 + 3	2 + 3	3
1 + 2	1 + 2 + 4	1 + 2 + 3 + 4	1 + 3 + 4	3 + 4
2	2 + 4	2 + 3 + 4	1 + 4	4

four-color key

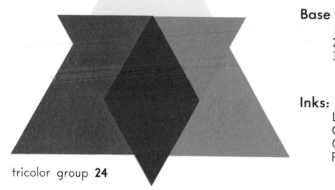

tricolor group **24**

MATCHING KEY

Base colors: *Index*
  1. process yellow **2**
  2. process red **6**
  3. brown **12**

Inks:	1.	2.	3.
Letterpress —	OP-2	OP-6	OP-12
Offset —	OPO-2	OPO-6	OPO-12
Gravure —	OPG-2	OPG-6	OPG-12
Flexographic —	OPF-2	OPF-6	OPF-12

A. group 24 plus red

B. group 24 plus chrome yellow

C. group 24 plus orange

D. group 24 plus gray

E. group 24 plus green

F. group 24 plus purple

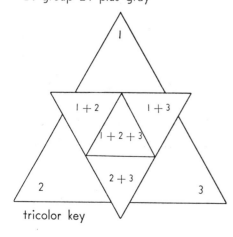

tricolor key

G. group 24 plus royal blue

H. group 24 plus process blue

MATCHING KEY

Base colors: *Index*
1. red **0**
2. chrome yellow **1**
3. purple **20**

Inks: **1.**   **2.**   **3.**

	1.	2.	3.
Letterpress	— OP-0	OP-1	OP-20
Offset	— OPO-0	OPO-1	OPO-20
Gravure	— OPG-0	OPG-1	OPG-20
Flexographic	— OPF-0	OPF-1	OPF-20

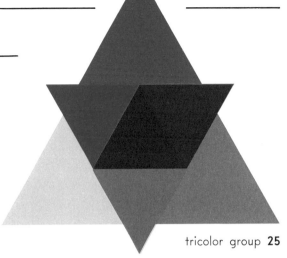

tricolor group **25**

A. group 25 plus process yellow

B. group 25 plus orange

C. group 25 plus process red

D. group 25 plus brown

E. group 25 plus gray

F. group 25 plus green

G. group 25 plus royal blue

H. group 25 plus process blue

1	1 + 3	1 + 2 + 3	2 + 3	3
1 + 2	1 + 2 + 4	1 + 2 + 3 + 4	1 + 3 + 4	3 + 4
2	2 + 4	2 + 3 + 4	1 + 4	4

four-color key

THE ANCIENT MARINER

Book decoration by Thomas F. Vroman
Color group 24G plus black (also groups 90D, 104D, 114C)
Rendering: Black key, India ink on illustration board. Color areas, India ink on
        heavy frosted acetate.
Process: Offset. Reduction, 5 to 3.

This decorative treatment of a classic subject provides an interesting contrast with the portrait on page 171, since the subject matter in each case is similar. There, aside from the fact that both are solid-color overprints, all similarity ceases. The two artists have used different renderings and completely different approaches, the one illustration being representational, the other bordering on the abstract.

The comparison serves to illustrate that overprinting is limited only by the artist's concept of its application. It should be remembered that the book itself is limited to comparatively few examples, but these examples suggest what may yet be produced when the infant craft matures.

It is to be hoped that more artists will emerge with Thomas Vroman's brilliant flair for decorative design, and that they will apply their talents to this new and fascinating art. Both Vroman and Joseph Low (see insert facing page 147) seem to have an innate grasp of what the printing press does best: the imparting of sharp, solid images, as in typography. Their style of design holds the suggestion of type itself, with a myriad of small symbols sprinkling the page to form the overall meaning of their compositions.

Thomas Vroman

tricolor group **26**

MATCHING KEY

Base colors:			Index
1. red			0
2. orange			4
3. gray			17

Inks:	1.	2.	3.
Letterpress	OP-0	OP-4	OP-17
Offset	OPO-0	OPO-4	OPO-17
Gravure	OPG-0	OPG-4	OPG-17
Flexographic	OPF-0	OPF-4	OPF-17

A. group 26 plus chrome yellow

B. group 26 plus process yellow

C. group 26 plus process red

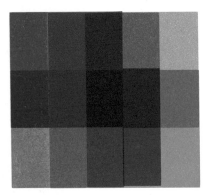

D. group 26 plus brown

E. group 26 plus green

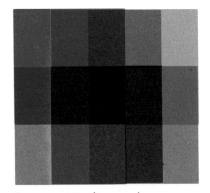

F. group 26 plus purple

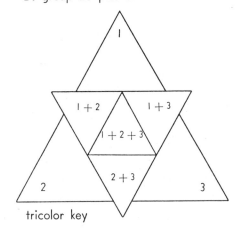

tricolor key

G. group 26 plus royal blue   **H.** group 26 plus process blue

MATCHING KEY

Base colors: *Index*
1. chrome yellow **1**
2. process yellow **2**
3. green **18**

Inks: **1.**   **2.**   **3.**
Letterpress — OP-1   OP-2   OP-18
Offset   — OPO-1   OPO-2   OPO-18
Gravure   — OPG-1   OPG-2   OPG-18
Flexographic — OPF-1   OPF-2   OPF-18

tricolor group **27**

A. group 27 plus red

B. group 27 plus orange

C. group 27 plus process red

D. group 27 plus brown

E. group 27 plus gray

F. group 27 plus purple

G. group 27 plus royal blue

H. group 27 plus process blue

1	1 + 3	1 + 2 + 3	2 + 3	3
1 + 2	1 + 2 + 4	1 + 2 + 3 + 4	1 + 3 + 4	3 + 4
2	2 + 4	2 + 3 + 4	1 + 4	4

four-color key

tricolor group **28**

MATCHING KEY

Base colors: *Index*
1. red 0
2. process yellow 2
3. purple 20

Inks: **1.**   **2.**   **3.**
Letterpress — OP-0   OP-2   OP-20
Offset   — OPO-0   OPO-2   OPO-20
Gravure   — OPG-0   OPG-2   OPG-20
Flexographic — OPF-0   OPF-2   OPF-20

A. group 28 plus chrome yellow

B. group 28 plus orange

C. group 28 plus process red

D. group 28 plus brown

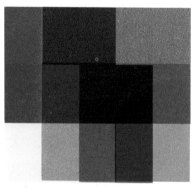

E. group 28 plus gray

F. group 28 plus green

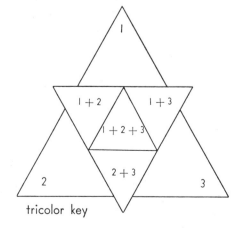

tricolor key

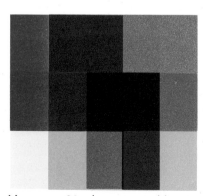

G. group 28 plus royal blue

H. group 28 plus process blue

MATCHING KEY

Base colors: *Index*
1. red 0
2. orange 4
3. green 18

Inks: **1.**   **2.**   **3.**

	1.	2.	3.
Letterpress	OP-0	OP-4	OP-18
Offset	OPO-0	OPO-4	OPO-18
Gravure	OPG-0	OPG-4	OPG-18
Flexographic	OPF-0	OPF-4	OPF-18

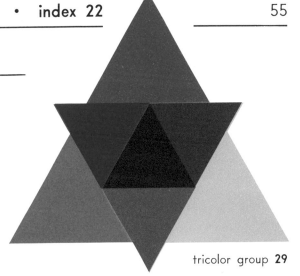

tricolor group **29**

A. group 29 plus chrome yellow

B. group 29 plus process yellow

C. group 29 plus process red

D. group 29 plus brown

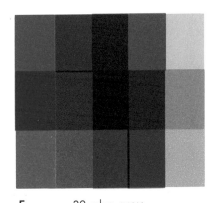

E. group 29 plus gray

F. group 29 plus purple

G. group 29 plus royal blue

H. group 29 plus process blue

1	1 + 3	1 + 2 + 3	2 + 3	3
1 + 2	1 + 2 + 4	1 + 2 + 3 + 4	1 + 3 + 4	3 + 4
2	2 + 4	2 + 3 + 4	1 + 4	4

four-color key

tricolor group **30**

MATCHING KEY

Base colors:　　　　*Index*
1. chrome yellow . . . .　1
2. orange . . . .　4
3. gray . . . .　17

Inks:	**1.**	**2.**	**3.**
Letterpress —	OP-1	OP-4	OP-17
Offset —	OPO-1	OPO-4	OPO-17
Gravure —	OPG-1	OPG-4	OPG-17
Flexographic —	OPF-1	OPF-4	OPF-17

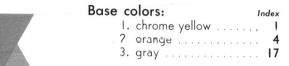

A. group 30 plus red

B. group 30 plus process yellow

C. group 30 plus process red

D. group 30 plus brown

E. group 30 plus green

F. group 30 plus purple

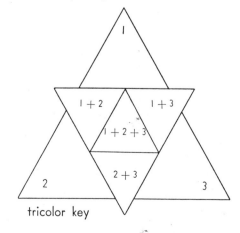
tricolor key

G. group 30 plus royal blue

H. group 30 plus process blue

MATCHING KEY

Base colors: *Index*
1. orange **4**
2. process red **6**
3. brown **12**

Inks:	**1.**	**2.**	**3.**
Letterpress	OP-4	OP-6	OP-12
Offset	OPO-4	OPO-6	OPO-12
Gravure	OPG-4	OPG-6	OPG-12
Flexographic	OPF-4	OPF-6	OPF-12

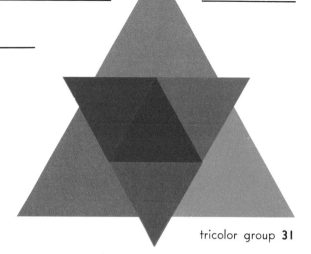

tricolor group **31**

A. group 31 plus red

B. group 31 plus chrome yellow

C. group 31 plus process yellow

D. group 31 plus gray

E. group 31 plus green

F. group 31 plus purple

G. group 31 plus royal blue

H. group 31 plus process blue

1	1 + 3	1 + 2 + 3	2 + 3	3
1 + 2	1 + 2 + 4	1 + 2 + 3 + 4	1 + 3 + 4	3 + 4
2	2 + 4	2 + 3 + 4	1 + 4	4

four-color key

SPANIEL IN THE LION'S DEN

Humorous juvenile book illustration by Tom Funk
Tricolor group 28 plus black
Rendering: Black key, pen and India ink on illustration board. Color areas, plastic
           stylus and color remover on Bourges sheets: 70% Process Yellow, 70%
           Poster Red, 70% Purple.
Process: Offset. No reduction.

For fanciful or whimsical illustrations of this kind, the decorative effect of solid-color treatment is ideal. It makes little difference which colors are used. A purple cow is just as acceptable as a magenta dog, and for a style like Tom Funk's, any attempt to use realistic color would be wrong.

Of particular interest in this case is the simplicity of the black key drawing. A few—very few—deft lines are sufficient to establish the picture. It is cartooning on a high level, with as much humor in the application of color as in the caricaturing of the animals. By reserving the pure red for a single, terrified spot in a sea of fiercely yellow lion hair, the artist has conveyed his idea to perfection.

Only five of the seven possible colors derived from tricolor group 28 are seen in this composition. The two missing colors are not needed. However, in a book printed with these three inks, the additional hues could be reserved for other illustrations, while in some cases certain of the colors shown here might be omitted. Thus considerable variety could be achieved within the limitations of a single set of transparent inks.

tricolor group **32**

MATCHING KEY

Base colors: *Index*
1. red 0
2. process red 6
3. gray 17

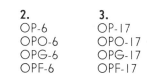

Inks: **1.**   **2.**   **3.**
Letterpress   — OP-0   OP-6   OP-17
Offset   — OPO-0   OPO-6   OPO-17
Gravure   — OPG-0   OPG-6   OPG-17
Flexographic — OPF-0   OPF-6   OPF-17

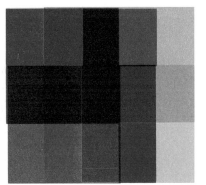

A. group 32 plus chrome yellow

B. group 32 plus process yellow

C. group 32 plus orange

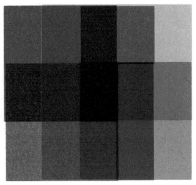

D. group 32 plus brown

E. group 32 plus green

F. group 32 plus purple

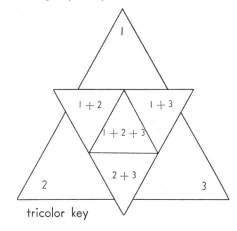

tricolor key

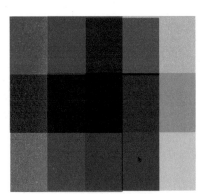

G. group 32 plus royal blue

H. group 32 plus process blue

MATCHING KEY

Base colors: *Index*
- 1. chrome yellow   1
- 2. process yellow **2**
- 3. purple **20**

Inks:	**1.**	**2.**	**3.**
Letterpress —	OP-1	OP-2	OP-20
Offset —	OPO-1	OPO-2	OPO-20
Gravure —	OPG-1	OPG-2	OPG-20
Flexographic —	OPF-1	OPF-2	OPF-20

tricolor group **33**

A. group 33 plus red

B. group 33 plus orange

C. group 33 plus process red

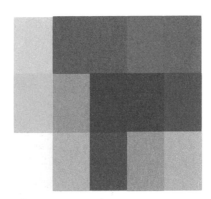

D. group 33 plus brown

E. group 33 plus gray

F. group 33 plus green

G. group 33 plus royal blue

H. group 33 plus process blue

1	1 + 3	1 + 2 + 3	2 + 3	3
1 + 2	1 + 2 + 4	1 + 2 + 3 + 4	1 + 3 + 4	3 + 4
2	2 + 4	2 + 3 + 4	1 + 4	4

four-color key

tricolor group **34**

MATCHING KEY

Base colors: *Index*
1. chrome yellow 1
2. orange , , , , , ... 1
3. green 18

Inks: **1.**   **2.**   **3.**
Letterpress — OP-1   OP-4   OP-18
Offset   — OPO-1   OPO-4   OPO-18
Gravure   — OPG-1   OPG-4   OPG-18
Flexographic — OPF-1   OPF-4   OPF-18

A. group 34 plus red

B. group 34 plus process yellow

C. group 34 plus process red

D. group 34 plus brown

E. group 34 plus gray

F. group 34 plus purple

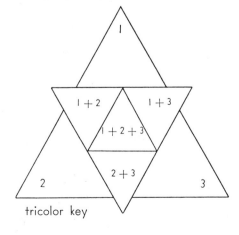

tricolor key

G. group 34 plus royal blue

H. group 34 plus process blue

MATCHING KEY

Base colors: *Index*
    1. process yellow **2**
    2. orange **4**
    3. gray **17**

Inks:	**1.**	**2.**	**3.**
Letterpress	— OP-2	OP-4	OP-17
Offset	— OPO-2	OPO-4	OPO-17
Gravure	— OPG-2	OPG-4	OPG-17
Flexographic	— OPF-2	OPF-4	OPF-17

tricolor group **35**

A. group 35 plus red

B. group 35 plus chrome yellow

C. group 35 plus process red

D. group 35 plus brown

E. group 35 plus green

F. group 35 plus purple

G. group 35 plus royal blue

H. group 35 plus process blue

1	1 + 3	1 + 2 + 3	2 + 3	3
1 + 2	1 + 2 + 4	1 + 2 + 3 + 4	1 + 3 + 4	3 + 4
2	2 + 4	2 + 3 + 4	1 + 4	4

four-color key

64

BLACK MAGIC—Pen and ink illustration by Donald E. Cooke as it appeared in *Sorcerer's Apprentice* (The John C. Winston Company). This drawing was made several years ago for black and white reproduction.

PLATE 4—purple. Working on a black reproduction proof of the line cut at left, the artist paints out areas where no purple is needed. Many of the purple areas will also appear on other plates to produce overprints.

PLATE 1—orange. Since this plate is to be used for a bright orange impression, several solid areas have been added to the drawing, particularly in the flames and also in those areas of light surrounding the caldron.

PLATES 1 plus 2—orange plus red. Here we see the beginning of the overprint. Parts of the illustration are still missing. These, of course, will be filled in with plates 3 and 4. The key plate in this case is purple.

PLATE 3—green. Another reproduction proof is given a treatment of opaque white to eliminate large areas. Note that some of the remaining portions of the drawing will register with portions of plates 1, 2, and 4.

PLATE 2—red. By reference to color chart 36F the artist can determine what to leave on each of the color plates to produce any one of the fifteen colors in that group. A few areas—such as the shoes—are filled in.

PLATES 1, plus 2, plus 3—orange, red, green. Darks are beginning to build up. Wherever green overprints the preceding colors, a deep tone results. Pure green and purple are reserved for small areas.

PLATES 1, plus 2, plus 3, plus 4—orange, red, green, purple. Drawing identical to the black and white print has been transformed into a multicolor illustration, not by sorcery, but by the magic of overprinting.

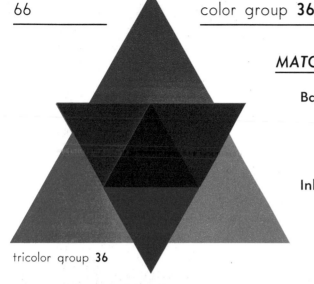

tricolor group **36**

MATCHING KEY

Base colors: *Index*
    1. red **0**
    2. orange **4**
    3. purple **20**

Inks: **1.**   **2.**   **3.**
    Letterpress — OP-0   OP-4   OP-20
    Offset   — OPO-0   OPO-4   OPO-20
    Gravure   — OPG-0   OPG-4   OPG-20
    Flexographic — OPF-0   OPF-4   OPF-20

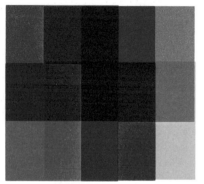

A. group 36 plus chrome yellow

B. group 36 plus process yellow

C. group 36 plus process red

D. group 36 plus brown

E. group 36 plus gray

F. group 36 plus green

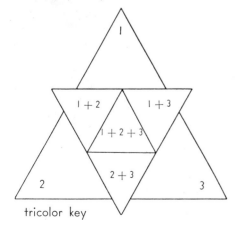

tricolor key

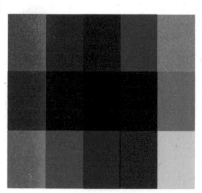

G. group 36 plus royal blue

H. group 36 plus process blue

MATCHING KEY

Base colors: *Index*
1. red 0
2. process red 6
3. green 18

Inks: **I.**   **2.**   **3.**
Letterpress — OP-0   OP-6   OP-18
Offset   — OPO-0   OPO-6   OPO-18
Gravure   — OPG-0   OPG-6   OPG-18
Flexographic — OPF-0   OPF-6   OPF-18

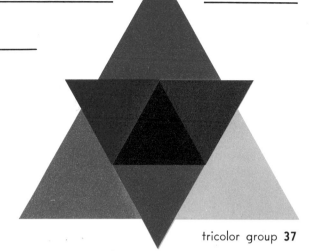

tricolor group **37**

A. group 37 plus chrome yellow

B. group 37 plus process yellow

C. group 37 plus orange

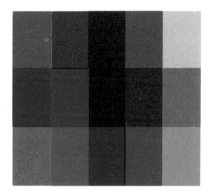

D. group 37 plus brown

E. group 37 plus gray

F. group 37 plus purple

G. group 37 plus royal blue

H. group 37 plus process blue

1	1 + 3	1 + 2 + 3	2 + 3	3
1 + 2	1 + 2 + 4	1 + 2 + 3 + 4	1 + 3 + 4	3 + 4
2	2 + 4	2 + 3 + 4	1 + 4	4

four-color key

tricolor group **38**

MATCHING KEY

Base colors: *Index*
1. chrome yellow   1
2. process red   6
3. gray   17

Inks:	**1.**	**2.**	**3.**
Letterpress —	OP-1	OP-6	OP-17
Offset —	OPO-1	OPO-6	OPO-17
Gravure —	OPG-1	OPG-6	OPG-17
Flexographic —	OPF-1	OPF-6	OPF-17

A. group 38 plus red

B. group 38 plus process yellow

C. group 38 plus orange

D. group 38 plus brown

E. group 38 plus green

F. group 38 plus purple

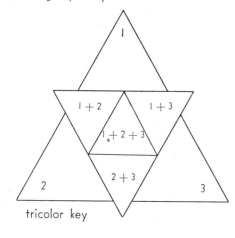

tricolor key

G. group 38 plus royal blue

H. group 38 plus process blue

MATCHING KEY

Base colors: *Index*
1. process yellow 2
2. orange 4
3. green 18

Inks: **1.**   **2.**   **3.**
Letterpress — OP-2   OP-4   OP-18
Offset — OPO-2   OPO-4   OPO-18
Gravure — OPG-2   OPG-4   OPG-18
Flexographic — OPF-2   OPF-4   OPF-18

tricolor group **39**

A. group 39 plus red

B. group 39 plus chrome yellow

C. group 39 plus process red

D. group 39 plus brown

E. group 39 plus gray

F. group 39 plus purple

G. group 39 plus royal blue

H. group 39 plus process blue

1	1 + 3	1 + 2 + 3	2 + 3	3
1 + 2	1 + 2 + 4	1 + 2 + 3 + 4	1 + 3 + 4	3 + 4
2	2 + 4	2 + 3 + 4	1 + 4	4

four-color key

tricolor group **40**

MATCHING KEY

Base colors: *Index*
1. chrome yellow **1**
2. orange **4**
3. purple **20**

Inks: **1.**   **2.**   **3.**

	1.	2.	3.
Letterpress —	OP-1	OP-4	OP-20
Offset —	OPO-1	OPO-4	OPO-20
Gravure —	OPG-1	OPG-4	OPG-20
Flexographic —	OPF-1	OPF-4	OPF-20

A. group 40 plus red

B. group 40 plus process yellow

C. group 40 plus process red

D. group 40 plus brown

E. group 40 plus gray

F. group 40 plus green

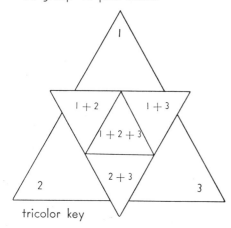

tricolor key

G. group 40 plus royal blue

H. group 40 plus process blue

MATCHING KEY

Base colors: *Index*
1. chrome yellow   1
2. process red   6
3. green   18

tricolor group **41**

Inks:	**1.**	**2.**	**3.**
Letterpress	OP-1	OP-6	OP-18
Offset	OPO-1	OPO-6	OPO-18
Gravure	OPG-1	OPG-6	OPG-18
Flexographic	OPF-1	OPF-6	OPF-18

A. group 41 plus red

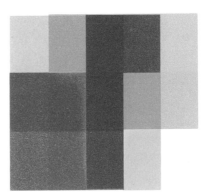

B. group 41 plus process yellow

C. group 41 plus orange

D. group 41 plus brown

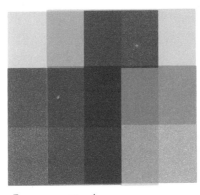

E. group 41 plus gray

F. group 41 plus purple

G. group 41 plus royal blue

H. group 41 plus process blue

1	1 + 3	1 + 2 + 3	2 + 3	3
1 + 2	1 + 2 + 4	1 + 2 + 3 + 4	1 + 3 + 4	3 + 4
2	2 + 4	2 + 3 + 4	1 + 4	4

four-color key

WAR DANCE

Costume plate by Edward F. Cortese
Color group 42H plus black (also groups 95E, 126D, 140C)
Rendering: Black areas, India ink on illustration board. Color areas, plastic stylus
and Bourges color remover on Bourges sheets: 70% Process Yellow,
70% Process Red, 50% Process Blue, 50% Black.
Process: Offset. No reduction.

One of the remarkable things about overprints is that they frequently suggest other, long-established art forms. *War Dance* is patterned after American Indian art, with its flat, decorative color areas and limited perspective.

The same qualities, so consciously developed in most oriental art, are closely allied to the basic principles of solid-color overprinting. Persian art, for example, could be beautifully reproduced or simulated by line overlays.

While this book is designed to show the vast potentialities and versatility of overprinting, there can be no question that one of its greatest uses will be for decorative treatment, since in that field there is no necessity for straining or forcing the medium into unsympathetic applications.

Here again is a picture in five inks which could be reduced to four by using a screen of black for the gray areas. (See illustrations on pages 42 and 43.) In this case the gray is all-important. It covers most of the picture area to tone down the brilliant colors except in a few well-chosen spots.

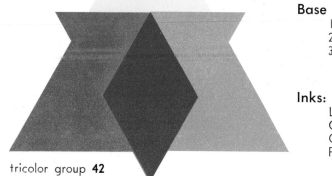

tricolor group **42**

MATCHING KEY

Base colors:　　　　　　　*Index*
　　1. process yellow **2**
　　2. process red **6**
　　3. gray **17**

Inks:　　　　　　　　**1.**　　　　**2.**　　　**3.**
　　Letterpress — OP-2　　OP-6　　OP-17
　　Offset — OPO-2　　OPO-6　　OPO-17
　　Gravure — OPG-2　　OPG-6　　OPG-17
　　Flexographic — OPF-2　　OPF-6　　OPF-17

A. group 42 plus red

B. group 42 plus chrome yellow

C. group 42 plus orange

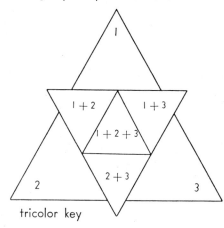

D. group 42 plus brown

E. group 42 plus green

F. group 42 plus purple

tricolor key

G. group 42 plus royal blue

H. group 42 plus process blue

MATCHING KEY

Base colors: *Index*
1. red 0
2. process red 6
3. purple 20

Inks: **1.**   **2.**   **3.**

	1.	2.	3.
Letterpress	OP-0	OP-6	OP-20
Offset	OPO-0	OPO-6	OPO-20
Gravure	OPG-0	OPG-6	OPG-20
Flexographic	OPF-0	OPF-6	OPF-20

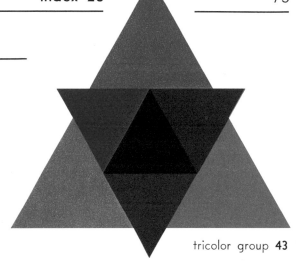

tricolor group **43**

A. group 43 plus chrome yellow

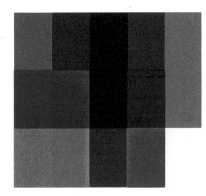

B. group 43 plus process yellow

C. group 43 plus orange

D. group 43 plus brown

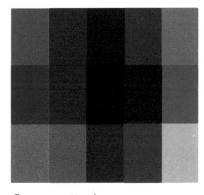

E. group 43 plus gray

F. group 43 plus green

G. group 43 plus royal blue

H. group 43 plus process blue

1	1 + 3	1 + 2 + 3	2 + 3	3
1 + 2	1 + 2 + 4	1 + 2 + 3 + 4	1 + 3 + 4	3 + 4
2	2 + 4	2 + 3 + 4	1 + 4	4

four-color key

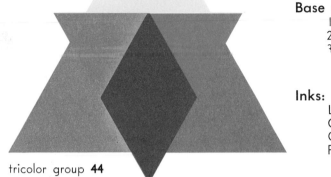

tricolor group **44**

MATCHING KEY

Base colors: *Index*

1. process yellow **2**
2. orange **4**
3. purple **20**

Inks:	**1.**	**2.**	**3.**
Letterpress —	OP-2	OP-4	OP-20
Offset —	OPO-2	OPO-4	OPO-20
Gravure —	OPG-2	OPG-4	OPG-20
Flexographic —	OPF-2	OPF-4	OPF-20

A. group 44 plus red

B. group 44 plus chrome yellow

C. group 44 plus process red

D. group 44 plus brown

E. group 44 plus gray

F. group 44 plus green

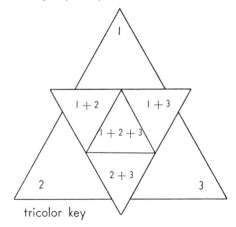

tricolor key

G. group 44 plus royal blue

H. group 44 plus process blue

MATCHING KEY

Base colors: *Index*
1. process yellow **2**
2. process red **6**
3. green **18**

Inks:	**1.**	**2.**	**3.**
Letterpress	OP-2	OP-6	OP-18
Offset	OPO-2	OPO-6	OPO-18
Gravure	OPG-2	OPG-6	OPG-18
Flexographic	OPF-2	OPF-6	OPF-18

tricolor group **45**

A. group 45 plus red

B. group 45 plus chrome yellow

C. group 45 plus orange

D. group 45 plus brown

E. group 45 plus gray

F. group 45 plus purple

G. group 45 plus royal blue

H. group 45 plus process blue

1	1 + 3	1 + 2 + 3	2 + 3	3
1 + 2	1 + 2 + 4	1 + 2 + 3 + 4	1 + 3 + 4	3 + 4
2	2 + 4	2 + 3 + 4	1 + 4	4

four-color key

78

THE SPARKLING GROVE

Magazine illustration by James Hill for *The Menace of Mr. Sampson*
Color group 45H plus black (also groups 95F, 129D, 142C)
Rendering: Black key, pen and India ink on illustration board. Color areas, stylus on Bourges sheets: 70% Process Yellow, 70% Process Red, 70% Green, 50% Process Blue.
Process: Offset. Reduction, 9 to 5.

Although little attempt has been made to use solid overprinting in national magazines, this example proves it is not only practical but strikingly effective. As part of a two-page spread in *Chatelaine,* the Canadian women's magazine, it was the outstanding page of the May 1954 issue. It suggests that we are on the threshold of a new departure in magazine illustration.

Printed by letterpress on coated paper in the original reproduction, it was nevertheless run with solid plates, except for the red, and also the gray tints on leaves and butterfly to the left of the main subject. Because full-strength process red was required on other pages of the magazine, the red plate for this illustration was made as a 70% screened tint.

In the accompanying offset reproduction the red plate is solid, but the ink itself is a lighter tint than the standard process red. Whenever possible, it is better to overprint with solids than with screened plates, since the result is cleaner and more brilliant.

Story illustration by
James Hill
from *Chatelaine* Magazine,
Art Director, Keith Scott.
Maclean-Hunter Publishing Co., Ltd.,
Toronto.

tricolor group **46**

MATCHING KEY

Base colors: *Index*
   1. chrome yellow   1
   2. process red   6
   3. purple   20

Inks: **1.**   **2.**   **3.**
Letterpress — OP-1   OP-6   OP-20
Offset   — OPO-1   OPO-6   OPO-20
Gravure   — OPG-1   OPG-6   OPG-20
Flexographic — OPF-1   OPF-6   OPF-20

A. group 46 plus red

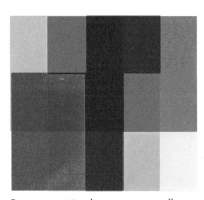

B. group 46 plus process yellow

C. group 46 plus orange

D. group 46 plus brown

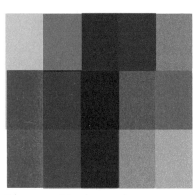

E. group 46 plus gray

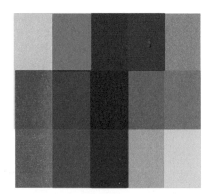

F. group 46 plus green

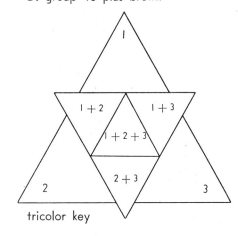

tricolor key

G. group 46 plus royal blue

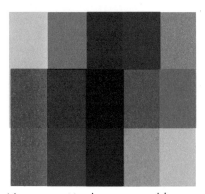

H. group 46 plus process blue

MATCHING KEY

Base colors:　　　　*Index*
1. orange 4
2. process red 6
3. gray 17

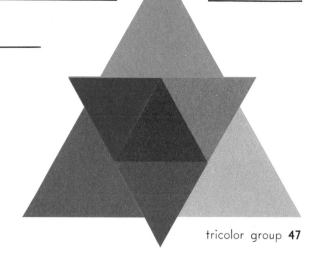

tricolor group **47**

Inks:　　　　　　**1.**　　　　**2.**　　　　**3.**
Letterpress — OP-4　　OP-6　　OP-17
Offset — OPO-4　　OPO-6　　OPO-17
Gravure — OPG-4　　OPG-6　　OPG-17
Flexographic — OPF-4　　OPF-6　　OPF-17

A. group 47 plus red

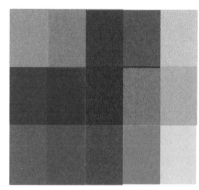

B. group 47 plus chrome yellow

C. group 47 plus process yellow

D. group 47 plus brown

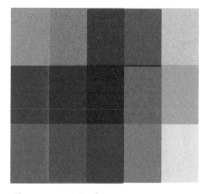

E. group 47 plus green

F. group 47 plus purple

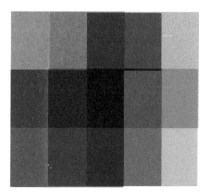

G. group 47 plus royal blue

H. group 47 plus process blue

1	1 + 3	1 + 2 + 3	2 + 3	3
1 + 2	1 + 2 + 4	1 + 2 + 3 + 4	1 + 3 + 4	3 + 4
2	2 + 4	2 + 3 + 4	1 + 4	4

four-color key

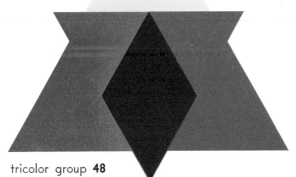

tricolor group **48**

MATCHING KEY

Base colors: *Index*
1. process yellow 2
2. process red 6
3. purple 20

Inks: **1.**   **2.**   **3.**

	1.	2.	3.
Letterpress —	OP-2	OP-6	OP-20
Offset —	OPO-2	OPO-6	OPO-20
Gravure —	OPG-2	OPG-6	OPG-20
Flexographic —	OPF-2	OPF-6	OPF-20

A. group 48 plus red

B. group 48 plus chrome yellow

C. group 48 plus orange

D. group 48 plus brown

E. group 48 plus gray

F. group 48 plus green

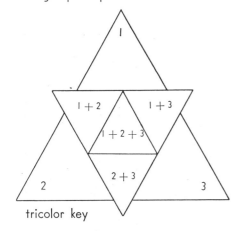

tricolor key

G. group 48 plus royal blue

H. group 48 plus process blue

MATCHING KEY

Base colors: *Index*
1. orange **4**
2. process red **6**
3. green **18**

Inks:	1.	2.	3.
Letterpress	— OP-4	OP-6	OP-18
Offset	— OPO-4	OPO-6	OPO-18
Gravure	— OPG-4	OPG-6	OPG-18
Flexographic	— OPF-4	OPF-6	OPF-18

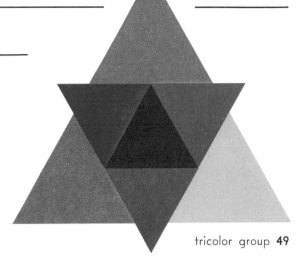

tricolor group **49**

A. group 49 plus red

B. group 49 plus chrome yellow

C. group 49 plus process yellow

D. group 49 plus brown

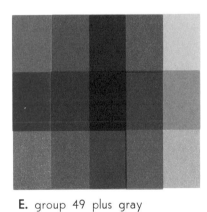

E. group 49 plus gray

F. group 49 plus purple

G. group 49 plus royal blue

H. group 49 plus process blue

1	1 + 3	1 + 2 + 3	2 + 3	3
1 + 2	1 + 2 + 4	1 + 2 + 3 + 4	1 + 3 + 4	3 + 4
2	2 + 4	2 + 3 + 4	1 + 4	4

four-color key

tricolor group **50**

MATCHING KEY

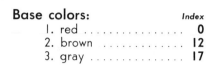

Base colors: *Index*
1. red 0
2. brown 12
3. gray 17

Inks:

	1.	**2.**	**3.**
Letterpress —	OP-0	OP-12	OP-17
Offset —	OPO-0	OPO-12	OPO-17
Gravure —	OPG-0	OPG-12	OPG-17
Flexographic —	OPF-0	OPF-12	OPF-17

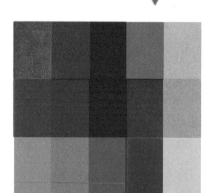

A. group 50 plus chrome yellow

B. group 50 plus process yellow

C. group 50 plus orange

D. group 50 plus process red

E. group 50 plus green

F. group 50 plus purple

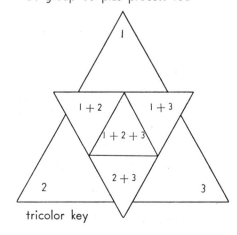

tricolor key

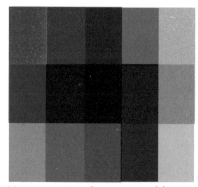

G. group 50 plus royal blue

H. group 50 plus process blue

MATCHING KEY

Base colors: *Index*
1. red 0
2. brown 12
3. green 18

Inks:

	1.	2.	3.
Letterpress	— OP-0	OP-12	OP-18
Offset	— OPO-0	OPO-12	OPO-18
Gravure	— OPG-0	OPG-12	OPG-18
Flexographic	— OPF-0	OPF-12	OPF-18

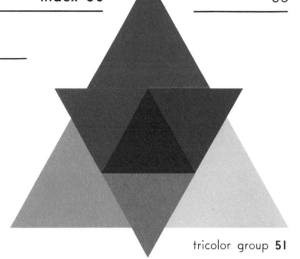

tricolor group **51**

A. group 51 plus chrome yellow

B. group 51 plus process yellow

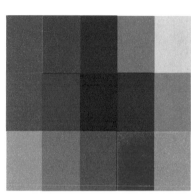

C. group 51 plus orange

D. group 51 plus process red

E. group 51 plus gray

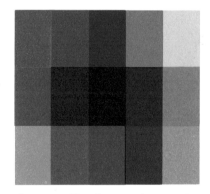

F. group 51 plus purple

G. group 51 plus royal blue

H. group 51 plus process blue

1	1 + 3	1 + 2 + 3	2 + 3	3
1 + 2	1 + 2 + 4	1 + 2 + 3 + 4	1 + 3 + 4	3 + 4
2	2 + 4	2 + 3 + 4	1 + 4	4

four-color key

HEIDI

by
Johanna Spyri

A World-Famous Classic Simply Told

ILLUSTRATED BY SUSAN KNIGHT

The John C. Winston Company

PHILADELPHIA   TORONTO

HEIDI

Book illustration and title page decoration by Susan Knight

Tricolor group 52 plus black

Rendering: Black key, pen and ink on illustration board. Color areas, plastic stylus on Bourges sheets: 70% Process Yellow, 70% Process Red, 50% Process Blue.

Process: Offset. No reduction.

This is a two-page spread from the PIXIE BOOK edition of *Heidi.* In the original, the process primaries—red, yellow and blue—were used, producing a bright, gay effect calculated to appeal to most children. Although it might have been preferable to show the example in its original colors, so many of the illustrations submitted were in the standard process inks that it seemed desirable to try a few variations and departures from the obvious color schemes.

In this case the more subdued colors are in keeping with the sensitive pen treatment of the key. That such drastic changes in color are possible, using the same plates or artwork, emphasizes the flexibility of overprinting. Without exception, the examples in this volume have been adapted to the single set of standardized colors without artistic loss. In some cases the illustrations have actually been improved by color modification.

To appreciate the significance of this it must be understood that the basic eleven inks of COLOR BY OVERPRINTING were selected for their effective use in the color charts *before* the illustrations were collected—a good indication that these standard colors can be applied successfully to a vast variety of printing problems and artistic effects.

tricolor group **52**

MATCHING KEY

Base colors: *Index*
1. chrome yellow 1
2. brown 12
3. gray 17

Inks:	1.	2.	3.
Letterpress —	OP-1	OP-12	OP-17
Offset —	OPO-1	OPO-12	OPO-17
Gravure —	OPG-1	OPG-12	OPG-17
Flexographic —	OPF-1	OPF-12	OPF-17

A. group 52 plus red

B. group 52 plus process yellow

C. group 52 plus orange

D. group 52 plus process red

E. group 52 plus green

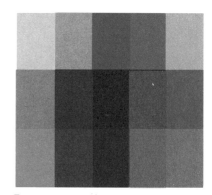

F. group 52 plus purple

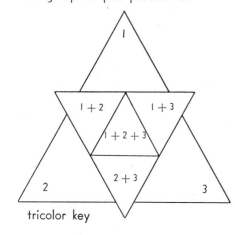

tricolor key

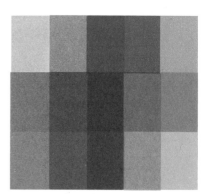

G. group 52 plus royal blue

H. group 52 plus process blue

SELECTIONS FROM THE READER'S DIGEST

No anthology of solid-color illustration would be complete without a representative selection of art from *The Reader's Digest,* which has developed an illustration program unique among today's magazines with national distribution.

Although most *Digest* illustration involves overprinting on a limited scale, the very fact that it is being printed on high-speed rotary presses, producing millions of copies, suggests that fruitful applications arc possible in magazine publishing generally. There is no reason to suppose that national weeklies can never develop solid-color overprint styles suited to their markets and to their own mechanical requirements. Although most magazine advertising in color calls for standard process yellow, red and blue, this does not rule out the possibility of changing over to "editorial color" in special forms devoted to illustrations and articles. Indeed, this change of pace—this separation of merchandising from story and entertainment—should be welcomed by editors and advertising managers alike.

It should be noted that the *Digest* places emphasis upon a "bookish" format involving well-designed, conservative typography which sets its pages apart from the more aggressive layout of a large national weekly. Nevertheless, the success of the *Digest* in the realm of solid multicolor printing is encouraging and makes a study of its pages worth-while for the art and printing technician. The *Digest* has done much to restore line illustration to a place of importance and dignity.

Reader's Digest first introduced multicolor line illustrations in its July 1948 issue; it has revealed progressive refinements in technique and style since that time. With the early introduction of a special set of editorial colors, the art directors set to work to encourage line artists to produce their own black and white separations for color. This was a serious undertaking, since not many artists were found capable of exercising multicolor separation techniques with ease and skill.

A few outstanding leaders in the field inspired the *Digest* staff. Attention was paid to Edy LeGrand, who began his climb to prominence as a stylistic illustrator in Paris in the 1920's, and to George Illian, the American illustrator who brought back to this country the fruits of his study and work abroad. The examples of the work of contemporary illustrators of note such as Edward Wilson, Henry Pitz and Howard Willard helped to give the project impetus. A small but impressive school of *Digest* artists began to develop an art pattern which is now the hallmark of the "great little magazine."

On the following pages are presented a few of the hundreds of exquisite* multicolor line illustrations produced for *Reader's Digest* and *Reader's Digest Condensed Books.*

color group 52A

JAMES ALEXANDER

Illustration for "When Are You Going To Turn Respectable?"
The Reader's Digest, July 1950.
Rendering: Black key, pen and India ink on a grainy-surfaced board. Color areas, litho crayon, brush and India ink rendered on the same material.
Reduction: None.

This is a fully developed overprint in the true-cat sense, and was one of the few examples submitted to demonstrate that the principle can be masterfully applied with standard black and white separations. A fine reward of tonality in the color areas has been made possible by the painstaking crayon buildup on the grained surface used for the separations.

HOWARD WILLARD

Illustration for "Nigeria—Land of Contrasts."
The Reader's Digest, March 1954.
Rendering: Black key—pen, brush and India ink on illustration board, with light-blue wash to show main color areas. Color overlays—pencil, dry brush, pen and ink, and white spatter stippling on heavy tracing paper. Some grained areas rendered with litho crayon on pieces of rough-surfaced illustration board pasted on the overlays.
Reduction: 2 to 1.

Here is a style of solid-color art executed with a freedom that would seem at first glance to verge on abandon. The swirls and flourishes in the separations are executed with a firm hand, however, and link together to produce a well-integrated pattern of color and line.

color group 52H

A STUDY IN CONTRASTS

On these facing pages the same illustrations are shown printed in two different color combinations and by two different processes. Those at the left have been reproduced by offset in standard colors of the Color by Overprinting charts, while the letterpress prints on this page are in *Reader's Digest* colors. The contrast is not presented to prove superiority of one group of colors over another, but to demonstrate that variations are possible, using the same set of plates or the same artwork. When two or more illustrations must be run together, it is sometimes necessary to make color compromises so that the number of impressions remains limited. Often by changing one or two of the colors, an illustration can be run successfully in inks required on other parts of the form, even though the artwork may not have been planned originally for those particular shades.

Both the offset and letterpress examples were run on two-color presses.

Inks used on this page:

Reader's Digest Fox (Brown). Bensing #68870.

Reader's Digest Acorn (Cream). Bensing #68871.

Reader's Digest Tomato (Red). Bensing #68873.

Reader's Digest Jordan (Green). Bensing #68874.

Reader's Digest Darkgray. Bensing #68876.

DAVID STONE MARTIN

Illustration for *A Man Called Peter.*

20 Reader's Digest Condensed Books.

Rendering: Black key, pen and ink on illustration board. Color overlays, India ink and black litho crayon on vinylite with a textured surface.

Process: Letterpress. Reduction, 6 to 5.

As in many *Digest* illustrations, bold areas of color are here superimposed on a delicate line drawing with pleasing finesse. There is a feeling of air and freedom, since no attempt is made to confine the color within precise limits. A rough-surfaced vinylite produced interesting crayon texture on the overlays, which can be seen as a dotted, or stippled, edge on each of the color plates. Overprinting is used sparingly, and in a sense, accidentally. The overprinted areas in the sky, for example, do not contribute in any way to the delineation of form, but they do provide delightful accidentals of additional color.

A delicate rendering of this kind requires the carefully balanced and restrained hues used so effectively by the *Digest.* Vivid colors could destroy the artist's sensitive feeling for his subject and would detract from the fine pen and ink treatment of the key.

ALDREN WATSON (opposite page, top)

Illustration for "Stay Put Young Man."

The Reader's Digest, July 1952.

Rendering: Brush and India ink on five separate overlays of heavy tracing paper, or "vellum."

Process: Letterpress. Reduction, 5 to 4.

Aldren Watson's decorative line drawings are always notable for their sharp, clean-cut quality; an appearance of being built with three-dimensional blocks of color—a style especially well suited to overprinting. In this case, although one of the colors is black, there is actually no key drawing. That is, none of the five separations could stand by itself as a complete, understandable pictorial unit. This interdependence of all colors, including black, gives Watson's solid-color illustrations a certain structural unity rarely found in art of this type.

Inks used on this page:

Reader's Digest Jordan (Green). Bensing #68874.

Reader's Digest Mountain (Blue). Bensing #68875.

Reader's Digest Darkgray. Bensing #68876.

Especially interesting for their variety of techniques, the illustrations on these facing pages represent three of the foremost line practitioners of our time. Each has illustrated books as well as contributed frequently to *Reader's Digest.* Henry Pitz is one of the most prolific illustrators of all time, having illustrated more than 160 books during the past 25 years.

HENRY C. PITZ (right)

Illustration for "My India."

Vol. XI *Reader's Digest Condensed Books.*

Rendering: All colors, brush and India ink on charcoal paper. Each color drawn over a light-table on a separate sheet, registered to the black key.

Process: Letterpress. Reduction, 2 to 1.

No artist has ever surpassed Henry Pitz in the handling of brush and ink. His variations in texture and line are astonishing, and anyone who has ever worked in the medium must marvel at the fine lines and perfect control he exhibits in rendering the tiniest detail. The method he uses for multi-color line separations is unique in that he combines the advantages of translucent overlays with the surface texture of handmade papers. By working on a light-table with paper that is sufficiently thin for light to penetrate at least two layers, he can register each color to his key and still retain the dry brush and other textural effects he likes to employ.

Inks used on this page:

Reader's Digest Fox (Brown). Bensing #68870.

Reader's Digest Acorn (Cream). Bensing #68871.

Reader's Digest Jordan (Green). Bensing #68874.

Reader's Digest Mountain (Blue). Bensing #68875.

Reader's Digest Darkgray. Bensing #68876.

MATCHING KEY

Base colors: *Index*
1. orange **4**
2. process red **6**
3. purple **20**

Inks:	**1.**	**2.**	**3.**
Letterpress	— OP-4	OP-6	OP-20
Offset	— OPO-4	OPO-6	OPO-20
Gravure	— OPG-4	OPG-6	OPG-20
Flexographic	— OPF-4	OPF-6	OPF-20

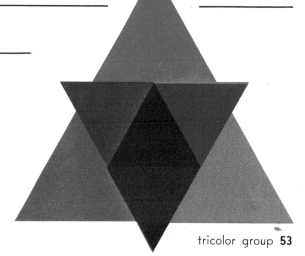

tricolor group **53**

A. group 53 plus red

B. group 53 plus chrome yellow

C. group 53 plus process yellow

D. group 53 plus brown

E. group 53 plus gray

F. group 53 plus green

G. group 53 plus royal blue

H. group 53 plus process blue

1	1 + 3	1 + 2 + 3	2 + 3	3
1 + 2	1 + 2 + 4	1 + 2 + 3 + 4	1 + 3 + 4	3 + 4
2	2 + 4	2 + 3 + 4	1 + 4	4

four-color key

tricolor group **54**

MATCHING KEY

Base colors: *Index*
1. chrome yellow   1
2. brown   12
3. green   18

Inks:	1.	2.	3.
Letterpress —	OP-1	OP-12	OP-18
Offset —	OPO-1	OPO-12	OPO-18
Gravure —	OPG-1	OPG-12	OPG-18
Flexographic —	OPF-1	OPF-12	OPF-18

A. group 54 plus red

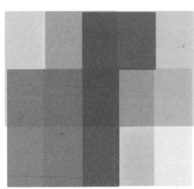

B. group 54 plus process yellow

C. group 54 plus orange

D. group 54 plus process red

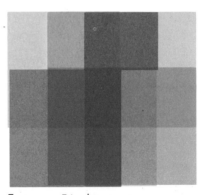

E. group 54 plus gray

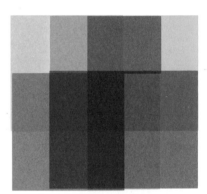

F. group 54 plus purple

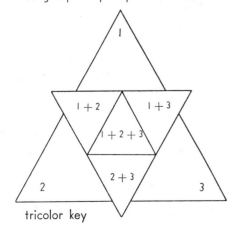

tricolor key

G. group 54 plus royal blue

H. group 54 plus process blue

MATCHING KEY

Base colors: *Index*
     1. process yellow 2
     2. brown 12
     3. gray 17

Inks: **1.**   **2.**   **3.**

	1.	2.	3.
Letterpress —	OP-2	OP-12	OP-17
Offset —	OPO-2	OPO-12	OPO-17
Gravure —	OPG-2	OPG-12	OPG-17
Flexographic —	OPF-2	OPF-12	OPF-17

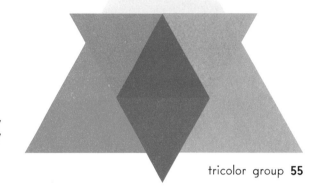

tricolor group **55**

A. group 55 plus red

B. group 55 plus chrome yellow

C. group 55 plus orange

D. group 55 plus process red

E. group 55 plus green

F. group 55 plus purple

G. group 55 plus royal blue

H. group 55 plus process blue

1	1 + 3	1 + 2 + 3	2 + 3	3
1 + 2	1 + 2 + 4	1 + 2 + 3 + 4	1 + 3 + 4	3 + 4
2	2 + 4	2 + 3 + 4	1 + 4	4

four-color key

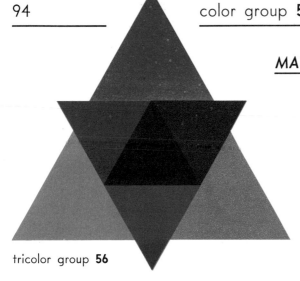

tricolor group **56**

MATCHING KEY

Base colors:			*Index*
1. red	. . . .		**0**
2. brown	. . . .		**12**
3. purple	. . . .		**20**

Inks:	**1.**	**2.**	**3.**
Letterpress —	OP-0	OP-12	OP-20
Offset —	OPO-0	OPO-12	OPO-20
Gravure —	OPG-0	OPG-12	OPG-20
Flexographic —	OPF-0	OPF-12	OPF-20

A. group 56 plus chrome yellow

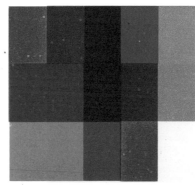

B. group 56 plus process yellow

C. group 56 plus orange

D. group 56 plus process red

E. group 56 plus gray

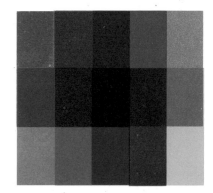

F. group 56 plus green

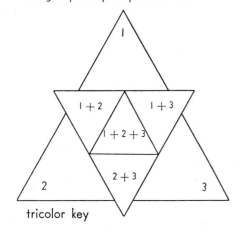

tricolor key

G. group 56 plus royal blue

H. group 56 plus process blue

MATCHING KEY

Base colors: *Index*
1. process yellow **2**
2. brown **12**
3. green **18**

Inks: **1.**   **2.**   **3.**

	1.	2.	3.
Letterpress —	OP-2	OP-12	OP-18
Offset —	OPO-2	OPO-12	OPO-18
Gravure —	OPG-2	OPG-12	OPG-18
Flexographic —	OPF-2	OPF-12	OPF-18

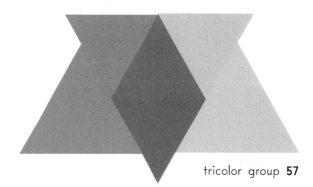

tricolor group **57**

A. group 57 plus red

B. group 57 plus chrome yellow

C. group 57 plus orange

D. group 57 plus process red

E. group 57 plus gray

F. group 57 plus purple

G. group 57 plus royal blue

H. group 57 plus process blue

1	1 + 3	1 + 2 + 3	2 + 3	3
1 + 2	1 + 2 + 4	1 + 2 + 3 + 4	1 + 3 + 4	3 + 4
2	2 + 4	2 + 3 + 4	1 + 4	4

four-color key

A VOYAGE TO BROBDINGNAG

Book illustration by Jacob Landau for *Gulliver's Travels*.
Color group 58F (also groups 19G, 111A, 117A)
Rendering: Scratchboard tools and stylus on Bourges sheets: 70% Poster Yellow,
        70% Poster Red, 70% Green, 70% Poster Blue.
Process: Offset. Reduction, 5 to 4.

Jacob Landau shows an excellent grasp of the inherent qualities of a new medium. Although this is his first transparent overprint, it is a fine example of brilliant technique as well as imaginative illustration. He shows no uncertainty in the handling of a startling and vivid composition.

The illustration deserves particular study by artists for its variety of textures, from bold, broad strokes of a flat-bladed stylus to the most delicate stippling of a finely pointed tool. Yet there is nothing self-conscious about the technique. The overall effect is of powerful unity and a surprisingly soft interplay of light and shade. This is achieved in some areas by a combination of treatments, where fine stippling of one color may be superimposed upon the bolder strokes of another.

From a printing standpoint also, this is an ideal example. It would be equally successful in offset or letterpress, since no large solid areas are overprinted in three or more colors. The breaking up of color by fine lines and dots on all but the yellow plate minimizes the problem of ink coverage as well as the danger of offset on the backs of sheets.

tricolor group **58**

MATCHING KEY

Base colors: *Index*
1. red **0**
2. chrome yellow **1**
3. royal blue **32**

Inks:	**1.**	**2.**	**3.**
Letterpress —	OP-0	OP-1	OP-32
Offset —	OPO-0	OPO-1	OPO-32
Gravure —	OPG-0	OPG-1	OPG-32
Flexographic —	OPF-0	OPF-1	OPF-32

A. group 58 plus process yellow

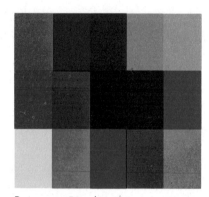

B. group 58 plus orange

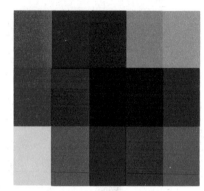

C. group 58 plus process red

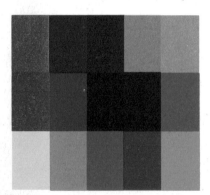

D. group 58 plus brown

E. group 58 plus gray

F. group 58 plus green

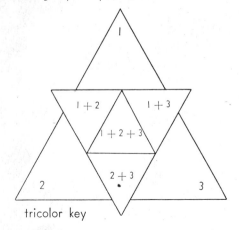

tricolor key

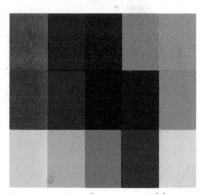

G. group 58 plus purple

H. group 58 plus process blue

MATCHING KEY

Base colors: *Index*
1. chrome yellow   1
2. brown 12
3. purple **20**

Inks: **1.**   **2.**   **3.**
Letterpress — OP-1   OP-12   OP-20
Offset   — OPO-1   OPO-12   OPO-20
Gravure   — OPG-1   OPG-12   OPG-20
Flexographic — OPF-1   OPF-12   OPF-20

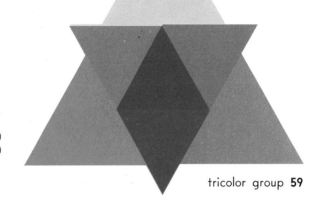

tricolor group **59**

A. group 59 plus red

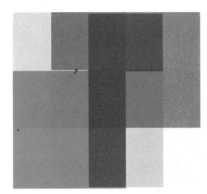

B. group 59 plus process yellow

C. group 59 plus orange

D. group 59 plus process red

E. group 59 plus gray

F. group 59 plus green

G. group 59 plus royal blue

H. group 59 plus process blue

1	1 + 3	1 + 2 + 3	2 + 3	3
1 + 2	1 + 2 + 4	1 + 2 + 3 + 4	1 + 3 + 4	3 + 4
2	2 + 4	2 + 3 + 4	1 + 4	4

four-color key

tricolor group **60**

MATCHING KEY

Base colors: *Index*
1. orange 4
2. brown 12
3. gray 17

Inks:

	1.	2.	3.
Letterpress —	OP-4	OP-12	OP-17
Offset —	OPO-4	OPO-12	OPO-17
Gravure —	OPG-4	OPG-12	OPG-17
Flexographic —	OPF-4	OPF-12	OPF-17

A. group 60 plus red

B. group 60 plus chrome yellow

C. group 60 plus process yellow

D. group 60 plus process red

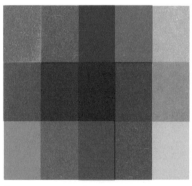

E. group 60 plus green

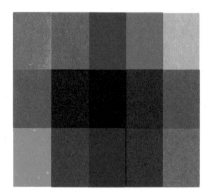

F. group 60 plus purple

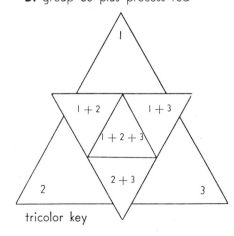

tricolor key

G. group 60 plus royal blue

H. group 60 plus process blue

MATCHING KEY

Base colors: *Index*
- 1. red **0**
- 2. process yellow **2**
- 3. royal blue **32**

Inks:	**1.**	**2.**	**3.**
Letterpress —	OP-0	OP-2	OP-32
Offset —	OPO-0	OPO-2	OPO-32
Gravure —	OPG-0	OPG-2	OPG-32
Flexographic —	OPF-0	OPF-2	OPF-32

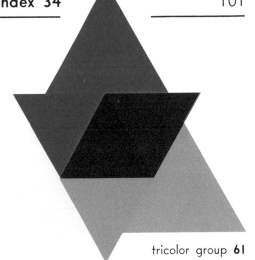

tricolor group **61**

A. group 61 plus chrome yellow

B. group 61 plus orange

C. group 61 plus process red

D. group 61 plus brown

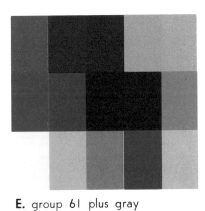

E. group 61 plus gray

F. group 61 plus green

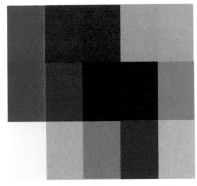

G. group 61 plus purple

H. group 61 plus process blue

1	1 + 3	1 + 2 + 3	2 + 3	3
1 + 2	1 + 2 + 4	1 + 2 + 3 + 4	1 + 3 + 4	3 + 4
2	2 + 4	2 + 3 + 4	1 + 4	4

four-color key

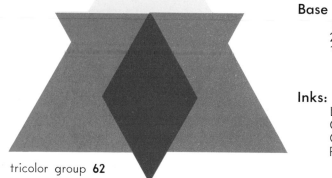

tricolor group **62**

MATCHING KEY

Base colors: *Index*
1. process yellow **2**
2. brown **12**
3. purple **20**

Inks:	1.	2.	3.
Letterpress	OP-2	OP-12	OP-20
Offset	OPO-2	OPO-12	OPO-20
Gravure	OPG-2	OPG-12	OPG-20
Flexographic	OPF-2	OPF-12	OPF-20

A. group 62 plus red

B. group 62 plus chrome yellow

C. group 62 plus orange

D. group 62 plus process red

E. group 62 plus gray

F. group 62 plus green

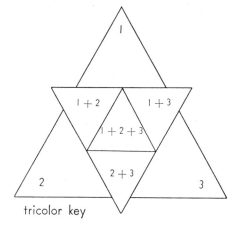

tricolor key

G. group 62 plus royal blue

H. group 62 plus process blue

MATCHING KEY

Base colors: *Index*
1. orange **4**
2. brown **12**
3. green **18**

Inks:	**1.**	**2.**	**3.**
Letterpress —	OP-4	OP-12	OP-18
Offset —	OPO-4	OPO-12	OPO-18
Gravure —	OPG-4	OPG-12	OPG-18
Flexographic —	OPF-4	OPF-12	OPF-18

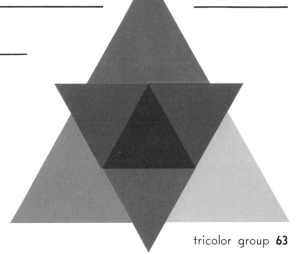

tricolor group **63**

A. group 63 plus red

B. group 63 plus chrome yellow

C. group 63 plus process yellow

D. group 63 plus process red

E. group 63 plus gray

F. group 63 plus purple

G. group 63 plus royal blue

H. group 63 plus process blue

1	1 + 3	1 + 2 + 3	2 + 3	3
1 + 2	1 + 2 + 4	1 + 2 + 3 + 4	1 + 3 + 4	3 + 4
2	2 + 4	2 + 3 + 4	1 + 4	4

four-color key

GLORIOUS FOURTH

Illustration by Albert Dorne
Tricolor group 64 plus black
Rendering: Key drawing, India ink on illustration board. Color areas, plastic
        stylus on Bourges sheets: 70% Poster Yellow, 70% Poster Red, 50%
        Process Blue.
Process: Offset. Reduction, 2 to 1. Overlays rendered actual size on reduced
        glossy print of key drawing.

Using Bourges sheets, many a black and white line drawing can be converted to a colorful overprint with comparative ease. The primary requisite is sufficient white area to permit effective use of additional color.

In this case, as shown in the accompanying small reproduction of the black key, the drawing is complete without color, and for many applications it would be just as effective in this form. Yet where a budget permits extra impressions or when a client demands the use of color, the same artwork may provide the foundation for color overlays. Certainly this scene suggests brilliant color and loses none of its original character by conversion.

Since the India ink drawing was considerably larger than the accompanying overprint, color overlays were rendered on a reduced glossy print, thus achieving a saving in time for the artist. Same-size plates were made from the reduced print and its Bourges overlays.

It will be noticed that only one or two minor corrections were made in the black drawing for its adaptation to color: portions of the flags were painted out, allowing the red stripes to show as pure color. In the platemaking, the black fields of the flags have been screened, permitting a percentage of blue to show. Otherwise the key drawing is identical to its original rendering.

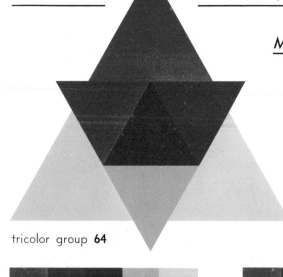

tricolor group **64**

MATCHING KEY

Base colors: *Index*
1. red **0**
2. chrome yellow **1**
3. process blue **34**

Inks:	**1.**	**2.**	**3.**
Letterpress —	OP-0	OP-1	OP-34
Offset —	OPO-0	OPO-1	OPO-34
Gravure —	OPG-0	OPG-1	OPG-34
Flexographic —	OPF-0	OPF-1	OPF-34

A. group 64 plus process yellow

B. group 64 plus orange

C. group 64 plus process red

D. group 64 plus brown

E. group 64 plus gray

F. group 64 plus green

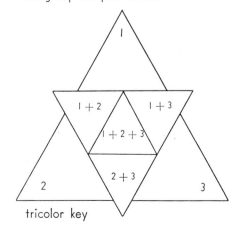

tricolor key

G. group 64 plus purple

H. group 64 plus royal blue

MATCHING KEY

Base colors: *Index*
1. red **0**
2. gray **17**
3. green **18**

Inks: **1.**   **2.**   **3.**

	1.	**2.**	**3.**
Letterpress	— OP-0	OP-17	OP-18
Offset	— OPO-0	OPO-17	OPO-18
Gravure	— OPG-0	OPG-17	OPG-18
Flexographic	— OPF-0	OPF-17	OPF-18

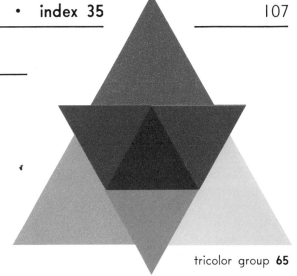

tricolor group **65**

A. group 65 plus chrome yellow

B. group 65 plus process yellow

C. group 65 plus orange

D. group 65 plus process red

E. group 65 plus brown

F. group 65 plus purple

G. group 65 plus royal blue

H. group 65 plus process blue

1	1 + 3	1 + 2 + 3	2 + 3	3
1 + 2	1 + 2 + 4	1 + 2 + 3 + 4	1 + 3 + 4	3 + 4
2	2 + 4	2 + 3 + 4	1 + 4	4

four-color key

tricolor group **66**

MATCHING KEY

Base colors:			Index
1. chrome yellow	....		1
2. process yellow	....		2
3. royal blue	....		32

Inks:	1.	2.	3.
Letterpress —	OP-1	OP-2	OP-32
Offset —	OPO-1	OPO-2	OPO-32
Gravure —	OPG-1	OPG-2	OPG-32
Flexographic —	OPF-1	OPF-2	OPF-32

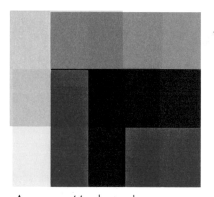

A. group 66 plus red

B. group 66 plus orange

C. group 66 plus process red

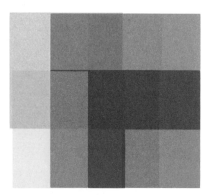

D. group 66 plus brown

E. group 66 plus gray

F. group 66 plus green

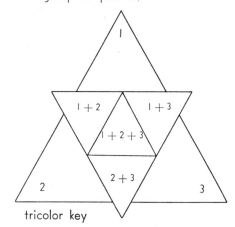

tricolor key

G. group 66 plus purple

H. group 66 plus process blue

MATCHING KEY

Base colors: *Index*
1. process red **6**
2. brown **12**
3. gray **17**

Inks: **1.**   **2.**   **3.**

	1.	2.	3.
Letterpress	— OP-6	OP-12	OP-17
Offset	— OPO-6	OPO-12	OPO-17
Gravure	— OPG-6	OPG-12	OPG-17
Flexographic	— OPF-6	OPF-12	OPF-17

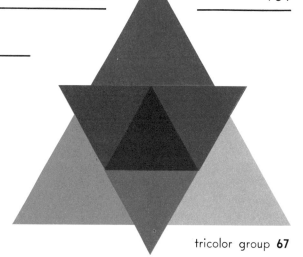

tricolor group **67**

A. group 67 plus red

B. group 67 plus chrome yellow

C. group 67 plus process yellow

D. group 67 plus orange

E. group 67 plus green

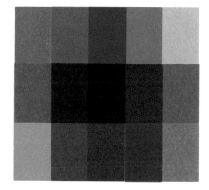

F. group 67 plus purple

G. group 67 plus royal blue

H. group 67 plus process blue

1	1 + 3	1 + 2 + 3	2 + 3	3
1 + 2	1 + 2 + 4	1 + 2 + 3 + 4	1 + 3 + 4	3 + 4
2	2 + 4	2 + 3 + 4	1 + 4	4

four-color key

ON PROTECTION FROM GOVERNMENT

Institutional space advertisement designed by Bradbury Thompson, used by permission of Container Corporation of America.

Tricolor group 68 plus black

Rendering: Original art not available. Plates were made from reproduction proofs of letterpress engravings.

Process: Offset. No reduction.

In the development of overprinting techniques it would be a serious mistake to assume that every design should be an elaborate pictorial composition. Actually the widest application of the principle may be in the field of simple design.

Mr. Thompson's striking advertising layout for Container Corporation of America demonstrates how the overprinting of design elements can be used with telling effect. This advertisement was run in national magazines, including *Time* and *Newsweek*, where the overprinting principle had to conform with a standard high-speed press run in process colors.

Once again we see illustrated the fact that artistic effectiveness bears no absolute relationship to the amount of expense in the reproduction process, nor to a limited or unlimited use of color. On the contrary, artistic success is measured solely by the artist's creative imagination and skill. Whether the problem is purely design or involves pictorial illustration, a masterpiece can be achieved in one color or one hundred colors. And artistic failures can run the same gamut.

Mr. Justice Lindley on Protection from Government

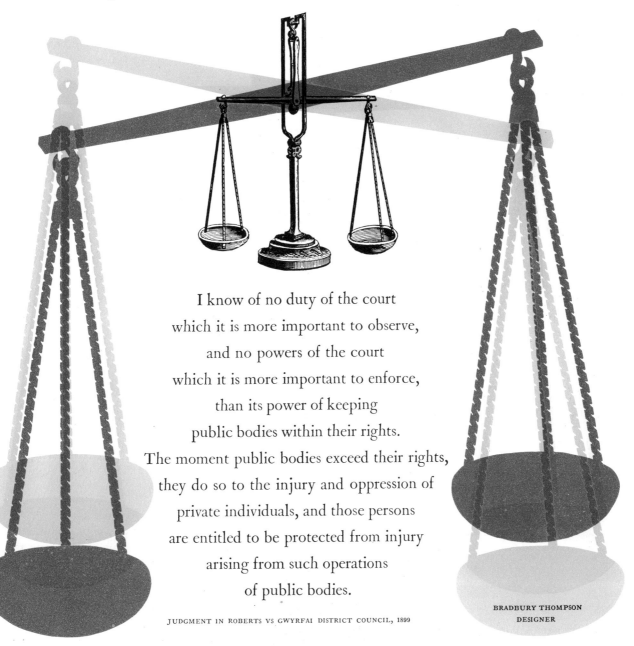

I know of no duty of the court
which it is more important to observe,
and no powers of the court
which it is more important to enforce,
than its power of keeping
public bodies within their rights.
The moment public bodies exceed their rights,
they do so to the injury and oppression of
private individuals, and those persons
are entitled to be protected from injury
arising from such operations
of public bodies.

JUDGMENT IN ROBERTS VS GWYRFAI DISTRICT COUNCIL, 1899

BRADBURY THOMPSON
DESIGNER

Container Corporation of America

tricolor group **68**

MATCHING KEY

Base colors: *Index*
  1. red **0**
  2. process yellow **2**
  3. process blue **34**

Inks: **1.**   **2.**   **3.**
Letterpress — OP-0   OP-2   OP-34
Offset   — OPO-0   OPO-2   OPO-34
Gravure   — OPG-0   OPG-2   OPG-34
Flexographic — OPF-0   OPF-2   OPF-34

A. group 68 plus chrome yellow

B. group 68 plus orange

C. group 68 plus process red

D. group 68 plus brown

E. group 68 plus gray

F. group 68 plus green

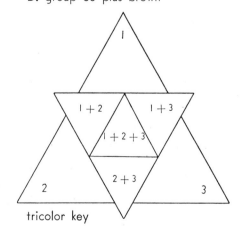

tricolor key

G. group 68 plus purple

H. group 68 plus royal blue

MATCHING KEY

Base colors: *Index*
1. red **0**
2. orange **4**
3. royal blue **32**

Inks: **1.**   **2.**   **3.**
Letterpress — OP-0   OP-4   OP-32
Offset — OPO-0   OPO-4   OPO-32
Gravure — OPG-0   OPG-4   OPG-32
Flexographic — OPF-0   OPF-4   OPF-32

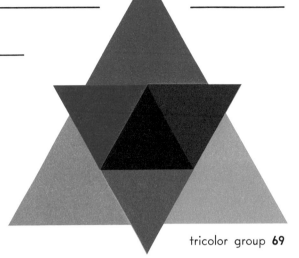

tricolor group **69**

A. group 69 plus chrome yellow

B. group 69 plus process yellow

C. group 69 plus process red

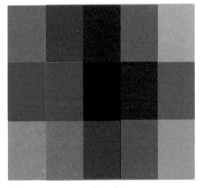

D. group 69 plus brown

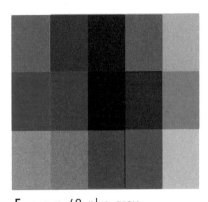

E. group 69 plus gray

F. group 69 plus green

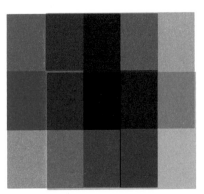

G. group 69 plus purple

H. group 69 plus process blue

1	1 + 3	1 + 2 + 3	2 + 3	3
1 + 2	1 + 2 + 4	1 + 2 + 3 + 4	1 + 3 + 4	3 + 4
2	2 + 4	2 + 3 + 4	1 + 4	4

four-color key

tricolor group **70**

MATCHING KEY

Base colors: *Index*
1. chrome yellow 1
2. gray 17
3. green 18

Inks:	1.	2.	3.
Letterpress —	OP-1	OP-17	OP-18
Offset —	OPO-1	OPO-17	OPO-18
Gravure —	OPG-1	OPG-17	OPG-18
Flexographic —	OPF-1	OPF-17	OPF-18

A. group 70 plus red

B. group 70 plus process yellow

C. group 70 plus orange

D. group 70 plus process red

E. group 70 plus brown

F. group 70 plus purple

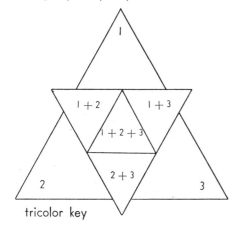

tricolor key

G. group 70 plus royal blue

H. group 70 plus process blue

MATCHING KEY

Base colors:　　　　　*Index*
1. orange **4**
2. brown **12**
3. purple **20**

Inks:	1.	2.	3.
Letterpress	— OP-4	OP-12	OP-20
Offset	— OPO-4	OPO-12	OPO-20
Gravure	— OPG-4	OPG-12	OPG-20
Flexographic	— OPF-4	OPF-12	OPF-20

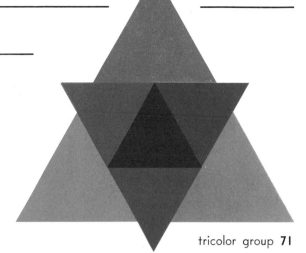

tricolor group **71**

A. group 71 plus red

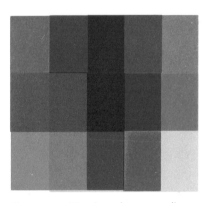

B. group 71 plus chrome yellow

C. group 71 plus process yellow

D. group 71 plus process red

E. group 71 plus gray

F. group 71 plus green

G. group 71 plus royal blue

H. group 71 plus process blue

1	1 + 3	1 + 2 + 3	2 + 3	3
1 + 2	1 + 2 + 4	1 + 2 + 3 + 4	1 + 3 + 4	3 + 4
2	2 + 4	2 + 3 + 4	1 + 4	4

four-color key

tricolor group **72**

MATCHING KEY

Base colors:			*Index*
1. process red			**6**
2. brown			**12**
3. green			**18**

Inks:	**1.**	**2.**	**3.**
Letterpress	OP-6	OP-12	OP-18
Offset	OPO-6	OPO-12	OPO-18
Gravure	OPG-6	OPG-12	OPG-18
Flexographic	OPF 6	OPF-12	OPF-18

A. group 72 plus red

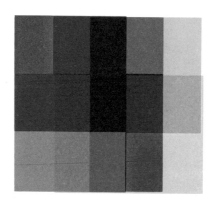

B. group 72 plus chrome yellow

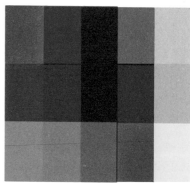

C. group 72 plus process yellow

D. group 72 plus orange

E. group 72 plus gray

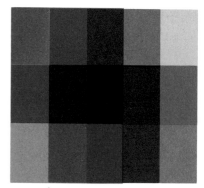

F. group 72 plus purple

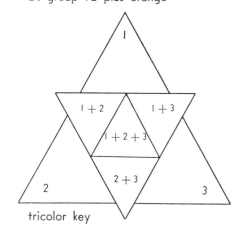

tricolor key

G. group 72 plus royal blue

H. group 72 plus process blue

MATCHING KEY

Base colors: *Index*
     1. red **0**
     2. gray **17**
     3. purple **20**

Inks:	**1.**	**2.**	**3.**
Letterpress —	OP-0	OP-17	OP-20
Offset —	OPO-0	OPO-17	OPO-20
Gravure —	OPG-0	OPG-17	OPG-20
Flexographic —	OPF-0	OPF-17	OPF-20

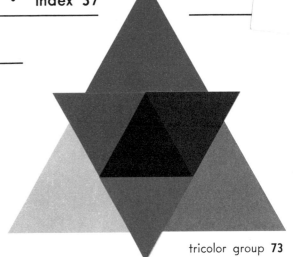

tricolor group **73**

A. group 73 plus chrome yellow

B. group 73 plus process yellow

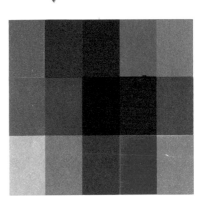

C. group 73 plus orange

D. group 73 plus process red

E. group 73 plus brown

F. group 73 plus green

G. group 73 plus royal blue

H. group 73 plus process blue

1	1 + 3	1 + 2 + 3	2 + 3	3
1 + 2	1 + 2 + 4	1 + 2 + 3 + 4	1 + 3 + 4	3 + 4
2	2 + 4	2 + 3 + 4	1 + 4	4

four-color key

tricolor group **74**

MATCHING KEY

Base colors: *Index*
  1. chrome yellow 1
  2. process yellow **2**
  3. process blue **34**

Inks: **1.**   **2.**   **3.**
  Letterpress — OP-1   OP-2   OP-34
  Offset   — OPO-1   OPO-2   OPO-34
  Gravure   — OPG-1   OPG-2   OPG-34
  Flexographic — OPF-1   OPF-2   OPF-34

A. group 74 plus red

B. group 74 plus orange

C. group 74 plus process red

D. group 74 plus brown

E. group 74 plus gray

F. group 74 plus green

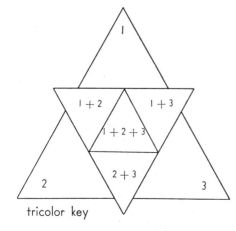

tricolor key

G. group 74 plus purple

H. group 74 plus royal blue

MATCHING KEY

Base colors: *Index*

     1. chrome yellow   1
     2. orange   4
     3. royal blue 32

Inks: **1.**   **2.**   **3.**

	1.	2.	3.
Letterpress	— OP-1	OP-4	OP-32
Offset	— OPO-1	OPO-4	OPO-32
Gravure	— OPG-1	OPG-4	OPG-32
Flexographic	— OPF-1	OPF-4	OPF-32

tricolor group **75**

A. group 75 plus red

B. group 75 plus process yellow

C. group 75 plus process red

D. group 75 plus brown

E. group 75 plus gray

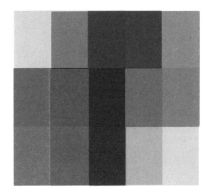

F. group 75 plus green

G. group 75 plus purple

H. group 75 plus process blue

1	1 + 3	1 + 2 + 3	2 + 3	3
1 + 2	1 + 2 + 4	1 + 2 + 3 + 4	1 + 3 + 4	3 + 4
2	2 + 4	2 + 3 + 4	1 + 4	4

four-color key

SHOWBOAT

Historical subject by Norman Guthrie Rudolph
Color group 75C (also groups 9G, 84C, 96B)
Rendering: Black areas, pen and ink on Traceoline overlay. Color areas, needle
        point and razor blade on Bourges sheets: 70% Poster Yellow, 100%
        Orange, 70% Process Red, 70% Poster Blue.
Process: Offset. No reduction.

Not every illustration assignment would allow sufficient time to carry out so detailed a rendering, but the effect achieved has almost the tonality of a painting. This is scratchboard technique on Bourges sheets, approaching what might be termed a handmade four-color halftone. Yet the effect of this picture is neither that of a halftone nor of an ordinary solid-color drawing, but is in a class by itself. The concentration of light which builds gradually to the white-gowned central figure is fine artistry, and is proof that infinite detail can be achieved with line overprinting.

For years Norman Rudolph has been recognized as a foremost water-colorist, and his treatment of an overprint is undoubtedly influenced by his career as a painter. Yet, working with a needle point on an unfamiliar medium, he has achieved a freedom that would be difficult to surpass.

Since much of the fine detail in this illustration is on the blue overlay, it was a difficult subject to photograph, but the detail for the blue plate was held by recontacting a thin negative in order to increase background density. Although this obviously involves greater cost than reproducing line plates from black and white copy, or strong color copy, it is still considerably less expensive than full-color process work.

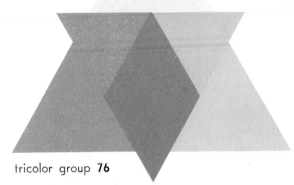

tricolor group **76**

MATCHING KEY

Base colors:		*Index*	
1. process yellow	. . . .	2	
2. gray	. . . .	17	
3. green	. . . .	18	

Inks:		**1.**	**2.**	**3.**
Letterpress	—	OP-2	OP-17	OP-18
Offset	—	OPO-2	OPO-17	OPO-18
Gravure	—	OPG-2	OPG-17	OPG-18
Flexographic	—	OPF-2	OPF-17	OPF-18

A. group 76 plus red

B. group 76 plus chrome yellow

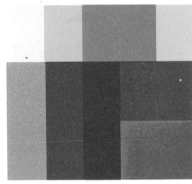

C. group 76 plus orange

D. group 76 plus process red

E. group 76 plus brown

F. group 76 plus purple

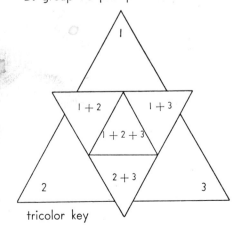

tricolor key

G. group 76 plus royal blue

H. group 76 plus process blue

MATCHING KEY

Base colors: *Index*
1. red **0**
2. orange **4**
3. process blue **34**

Inks: **1.**   **2.**   **3.**

	1.	2.	3.
Letterpress	OP-0	OP-4	OP-34
Offset	OPO-0	OPO-4	OPO-34
Gravure	OPG-0	OPG-4	OPG-34
Flexographic	OPF-0	OPF-4	OPF-34

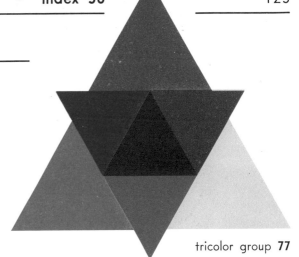

tricolor group **77**

A. group 77 plus chrome yellow

B. group 77 plus process yellow

C. group 77 plus process red

D. group 77 plus brown

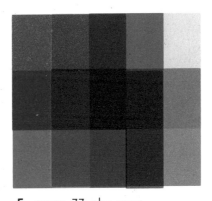

E. group 77 plus gray

F. group 77 plus green

G. group 77 plus purple

H. group 77 plus royal blue

1	1 + 3	1 + 2 + 3	2 + 3	3
1 + 2	1 + 2 + 4	1 + 2 + 3 + 4	1 + 3 + 4	3 + 4
2	2 + 4	2 + 3 + 4	1 + 4	4

four-color key

tricolor group **78**

MATCHING KEY

Base colors: *Index*
1. red **0**
2. process red **6**
3. royal blue **32**

Inks:	1.	2.	3.
Letterpress —	OP-0	OP-6	OP-32
Offset —	OPO-0	OPO-6	OPO-32
Gravure —	OPG-0	OPG-6	OPG-32
Flexographic —	OPГ-0	OPF-6	OPF-32

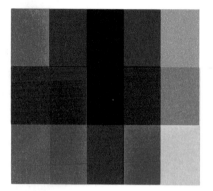

A. group 78 plus chrome yellow

B. group 78 plus process yellow

C. group 78 plus orange

D. group 78 plus brown

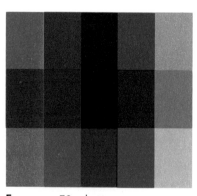

E. group 78 plus gray

F. group 78 plus green

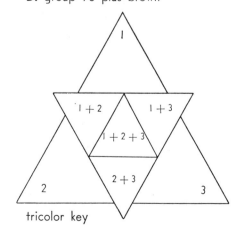

tricolor key

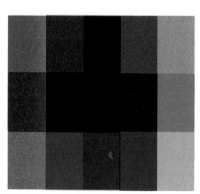

G. group 78 plus purple

H. group 78 plus process blue

MATCHING KEY

Base colors: *Index*
1. red **0**
2. green **18**
3. purple **20**

Inks:

	1.	**2.**	**3.**
Letterpress	— OP-0	OP-18	OP-20
Offset	— OPO-0	OPO-18	OPO-20
Gravure	— OPG-0	OPG-18	OPG-20
Flexographic	— OPF-0	OPF-18	OPF-20

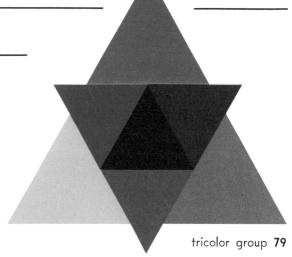

tricolor group **79**

A. group 79 plus chrome yellow

B. group 79 plus process yellow

C. group 79 plus orange

D. group 79 plus process red

E. group 79 plus brown

F. group 79 plus gray

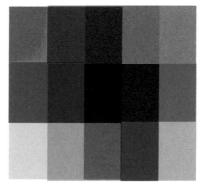

G. group 79 plus royal blue

H. group 79 plus process blue

1	1 + 3	1 + 2 + 3	2 + 3	3
1 + 2	1 + 2 + 4	1 + 2 + 3 + 4	1 + 3 + 4	3 + 4
2	2 + 4	2 + 3 + 4	1 + 4	4

four-color key

THE LITTLEST CHRISTMAS TREE

Book jacket design by Donald E. Cooke, from the book by Flora Strousse. Illustration used by permission of Morehouse-Gorham Company.
Tricolor group 79
Rendering: Plastic stylus on Bourges sheets: 70% Poster Red, 70% Green, 70% Purple.
Process: Offset. No reduction.

Employing only three colors, this book jacket suggests how much can be done under a limited plate and presswork budget. Although most of the examples in COLOR BY OVERPRINTING are made up of at least four inks, the possibilities of simpler palettes should not be overlooked. Actually, with seven distinct colors available to the artist who works within the limits of a given tricolor group, many beautiful and colorful compositions may be worked out.

The design was originally printed by offset on coated stock. Despite this fact, and the fact that some heavy areas contain all three inks, or 300% buildup of solids, the finished jackets were put on the books with no protective coating of varnish or lamination. Some rubbing occurred on a few copies in the course of packing and shipping, but for the most part the percentage of damaged jackets was remarkably low.

For best results, however, any overprint that is destined to be handled should at least be varnished or lacquered.

In some cases, overprint book jackets have been run successfully with a high percentage of varnish in the inks themselves. Such problems should be discussed with the ink manufacturer before a job goes to press.

This is believed to be the first line overprint ever to be produced without the use of a black or dark-colored key drawing, and with the dark areas built entirely by the overprinting of bright-colored transparent inks.

THE littlest
CHRISTMAS
TREE

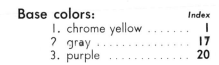

tricolor group **80**

MATCHING KEY

Base colors: *Index*
1. chrome yellow 1
? gray **17**
3. purple **20**

Inks:

	1.	2.	3.
Letterpress	OP-1	OP-17	OP-20
Offset	OPO-1	OPO-17	OPO-20
Gravure	OPG-1	OPG-17	OPG-20
Flexographic	OPF-1	OPF-17	OPF-20

A. group 80 plus red

B. group 80 plus process yellow

C. group 80 plus orange

D. group 80 plus process red

E. group 80 plus brown

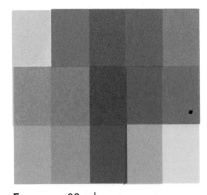

F. group 80 plus green

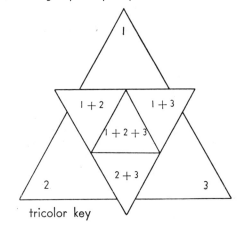

tricolor key

G. group 80 plus royal blue

H. group 80 plus process blue

MATCHING KEY

Base colors: *Index*
1. process yellow **2**
2. orange **4**
3. royal blue **32**

Inks:	**1.**	**2.**	**3.**
Letterpress —	OP-2	OP-4	OP-32
Offset —	OPO-2	OPO-4	OPO-32
Gravure —	OPG-2	OPG-4	OPG-32
Flexographic —	OPF-2	OPF-4	OPF-32

tricolor group **81**

A. group 81 plus red

B. group 81 plus chrome yellow

C. group 81 plus process red

D. group 81 plus brown

E. group 81 plus gray

F. group 81 plus green

G. group 81 plus purple

H. group 81 plus process blue

1	1 + 3	1 + 2 + 3	2 + 3	3
1 + 2	1 + 2 + 4	1 + 2 + 3 + 4	1 + 3 + 4	3 + 4
2	2 + 4	2 + 3 + 4	1 + 4	4

four-color key

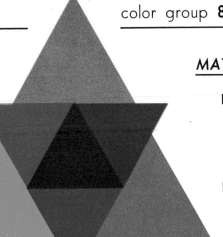

tricolor group **82**

MATCHING KEY

Base colors:		*Index*	
1. process red	....	**6**	
2. brown	....	**12**	
3. purple	....	**20**	

Inks:	**1.**	**2.**	**3.**
Letterpress —	OP-6	OP-12	OP-20
Offset —	OPO-6	OPO-12	OPO-20
Gravure —	OPG-6	OPG-12	OPG-20
Flexographic —	OPF-6	OPF-12	OPF-20

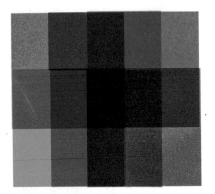

A. group 82 plus red

B. group 82 plus chrome yellow

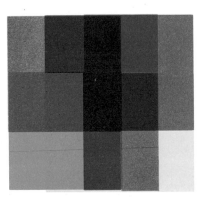

C. group 82 plus process yellow

D. group 82 plus orange

E. group 82 plus gray

F. group 82 plus green

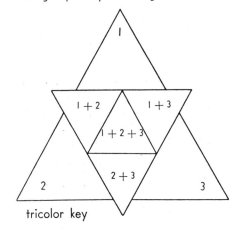

tricolor key

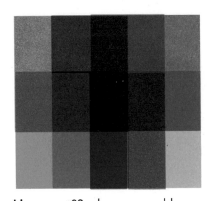

G. group 82 plus royal blue

H. group 82 plus process blue

MATCHING KEY

Base colors: *Index*
   1. chrome yellow   1
   2. orange   4
   3. process blue   34

Inks: **1.**   **2.**   **3.**
   Letterpress   — OP-1   OP-4   OP-34
   Offset   — OPO-1   OPO-4   OPO-34
   Gravure   — OPG-1   OPG-4   OPG-34
   Flexographic — OPF-1   OPF-4   OPF-34

tricolor group **83**

A. group 83 plus red

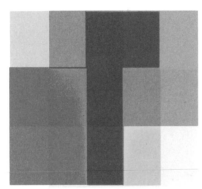

B. group 83 plus process yellow

C. group 83 plus process red

D. group 83 plus brown

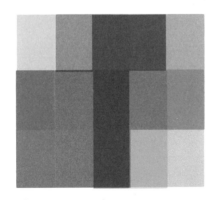

E. group 83 plus gray

F. group 83 plus green

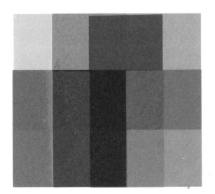

G. group 83 plus purple

H. group 83 plus royal blue

1	1 + 3	1 + 2 + 3	2 + 3	3
1 + 2	1 + 2 + 4	1 + 2 + 3 + 4	1 + 3 + 4	3 + 4
2	2 + 4	2 + 3 + 4	1 + 4	4

four-color key

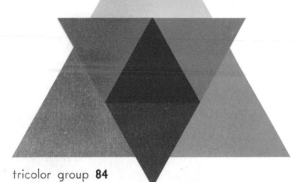

tricolor group **84**

MATCHING KEY

Base colors: *Index*
1. chrome yellow 1
2. process red **6**
3. royal blue **32**

Inks:

	1.	**2.**	**3.**
Letterpress	— OP-1	OP-6	OP-32
Offset	— OPO-1	OPO-6	OPO-32
Gravure	— OPG-1	OPG-6	OPG-32
Flexographic	— OPF-1	OPF-6	OPF-32

A. group 84 plus red

B. group 84 plus process yellow

C. group 84 plus orange

D. group 84 plus brown

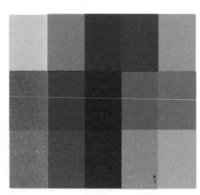

E. group 84 plus gray

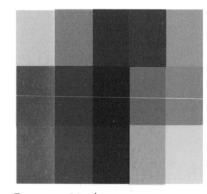

F. group 84 plus green

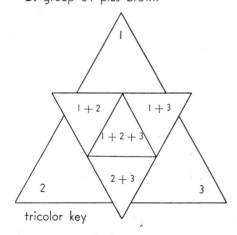

tricolor key

G. group 84 plus purple

H. group 84 plus process blue

MATCHING KEY

Base colors:　　　　　*Index*
1. chrome yellow 1
2. green 18
3. purple 20

Inks:	**1.**	**2.**	**3.**
Letterpress —	OP-1	OP-18	OP-20
Offset —	OPO-1	OPO-18	OPO-20
Gravure —	OPG-1	OPG-18	OPG-20
Flexographic —	OPF-1	OPF-18	OPF-20

tricolor group **85**

A. group 85 plus red

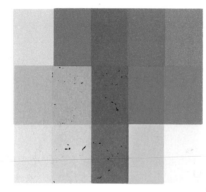

B. group 85 plus process yellow

C. group 85 plus orange

D. group 85 plus process red

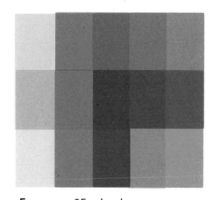

E. group 85 plus brown

F. group 85 plus gray

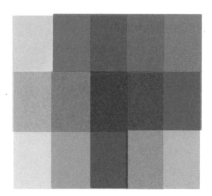

G. group 85 plus royal blue

H. group 85 plus process blue

1	1 + 3	1 + 2 + 3	2 + 3	3
1 + 2	1 + 2 + 4	1 + 2 + 3 + 4	1 + 3 + 4	3 + 4
2	2 + 4	2 + 3 + 4	1 + 4	4

four-color key

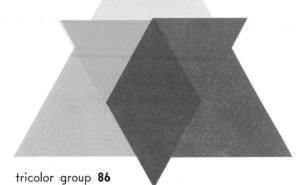

tricolor group **86**

MATCHING KEY

Base colors: *Index*
1. process yellow **2**
2. gray **17**
3. purple **20**

Inks:	**1.**	**2.**	**3.**
Letterpress —	OP-2	OP-17	OP-20
Offset —	OPO-2	OPO-17	OPO-20
Gravure —	OPG-2	OPG-17	OPG-20
Flexographic —	OPF-2	OPF-17	OPF-20

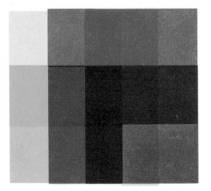

A. group 86 plus red

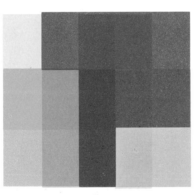

B. group 86 plus chrome yellow

C. group 86 plus orange

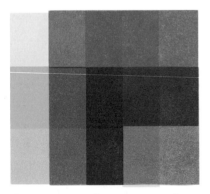

D. group 86 plus process red

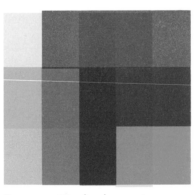

E. group 86 plus brown

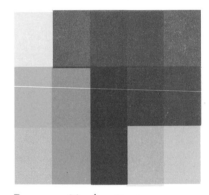

F. group 86 plus green

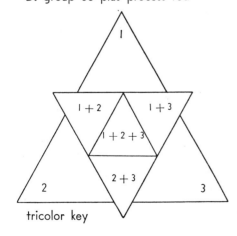

tricolor key

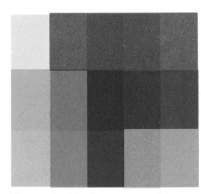

G. group 86 plus royal blue

H. group 86 plus process blue

MATCHING KEY

Base colors: *Index*
1. orange **4**
2. gray **17**
3. green **18**

Inks: **1.**   **2.**   **3.**
Letterpress — OP-4   OP-17   OP-18
Offset — OPO-4   OPO-17   OPO-18
Gravure — OPG-4   OPG-17   OPG-18
Flexographic — OPF-4   OPF-17   OPF-18

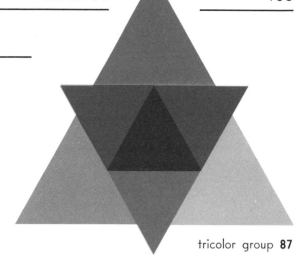

tricolor group **87**

A. group 87 plus red

B. group 87 plus chrome yellow

C. group 87 plus process yellow

D. group 87 plus process red

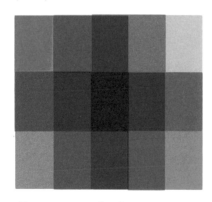

E. group 87 plus brown

F. group 87 plus purple

G. group 87 plus royal blue

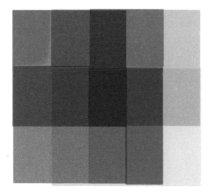

H. group 87 plus process blue

1	1 + 3	1 + 2 + 3	2 + 3	3
1 + 2	1 + 2 + 4	1 + 2 + 3 + 4	1 + 3 + 4	3 + 4
2	2 + 4	2 + 3 + 4	1 + 4	4

four-color key

THESE ARE THE TOOLS

Space advertising design by Paul Darrow, Art Director. Courtesy N. W. Ayer &
Son, Inc.

Color group 88B plus black (also groups 6H, 68C, 95A)

Rendering: India ink on illustration board. Five separate drawings, one for each
color. Register maintained by careful tracing of the design elements
on each board.

Process: Offset. No reduction.

More and more frequently the principles of abstract design are being applied
to advertising, where the impact of a simple message can be conveyed by means of
a few decorative symbols. Here is an advertisement especially designed for COLOR BY
OVERPRINTING by one of the foremost advertising agencies in the United States. Good
design and forceful copy are skilfully welded.

If such an advertisement were to appear in a nationally circulated magazine, it
would probably be printed by letterpress on a coated paper. Three of the colors
chosen are the standard "process" red, yellow and blue. Although the addition of a
second red increases the color range of this particular design, it would not be essential if the number of impressions were more limited.

The artwork was drawn in India ink on five separate pieces of illustration board,
after a color comprehensive was worked out, using adhesive-backed Bourges sheets.
Since the color areas for each plate are comparatively simple, the use of overlays
was not required, and the artist was able to do a precise rendering in black, using
the conventional tools depicted in the design itself: triangle, T-square, brush and ink.

No mastery of new overlay techniques is needed for this type of job. The artist's
"wit and imagination" are the principle ingredients.

These are tools
of the trade.
When applied with
wit, knowledge,
and imagination,
upon a basis of
research, they
produce good
advertising.

N W A Y E R

tricolor group **88**

MATCHING KEY

Base colors: *Index*
1. red **0**
2. process red **6**
3. process blue **34**

Inks:	**1.**	**2.**	**3.**
Letterpress —	OP-0	OP-6	OP-34
Offset —	OPO-0	OPO-6	OPO-34
Gravure —	OPG-0	OPG-6	OPG-34
Flexographic —	OPF-0	OPF-6	OPF-34

A. group 88 plus chrome yellow

B. group 88 plus process yellow

C. group 88 plus orange

D. group 88 plus brown

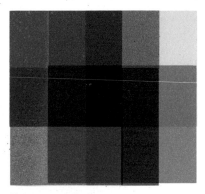

E. group 88 plus gray

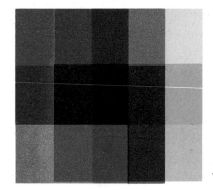

F. group 88 plus green

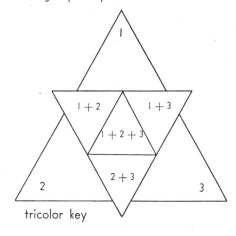

tricolor key

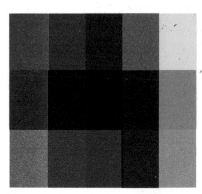

G. group 88 plus purple

H. group 88 plus royal blue

MATCHING KEY

Base colors: *Index*
1. process yellow **2**
2. orange **4**
3. process blue **34**

Inks: **1.**   **2.**   **3.**
Letterpress — OP-2   OP-4   OP-34
Offset   — OPO-2   OPO-4   OPO-34
Gravure   — OPG-2   OPG-4   OPG-34
Flexographic — OPF-2   OPF-4   OPF-34

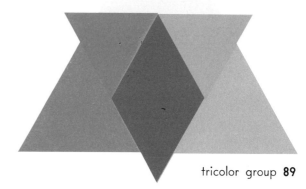

tricolor group **89**

A. group 89 plus red

B. group 89 plus chrome yellow

C. group 89 plus process red

D. group 89 plus brown

E. group 89 plus gray

F. group 89 plus green

G. group 89 plus purple

H. group 89 plus royal blue

1	1 + 3	1 + 2 + 3	2 + 3	3
1 + 2	1 + 2 + 4	1 + 2 + 3 + 4	1 + 3 + 4	3 + 4
2	2 + 4	2 + 3 + 4	1 + 4	4

four-color key

DESIGN FROM THE DEEP

Study of seashells by Edward A. Wilson
Color group 90 plus black
Rendering: Black key, brush and India ink on illustration board. Color areas,
                 stylus and Bourges color remover on Bourges sheets: 70% Process
                 Yellow, 70% Process Red, 70% Poster Blue.
Process: Offset. Reduction, 5 to 4.

When Edward Wilson was asked to do an overprint, he was given complete freedom in his choice of subject. It was to be expected that a man who has illustrated *Treasure Island* and other sea stories might select a marine subject, but for one who draws ships and who does figure compositions so expertly, this remarkable still life represents a surprising departure.

With the sensuous beauty of abstract design, the pattern of form and color is a source of endless satisfaction and delight. The colors themselves are perfectly balanced, with the pure colors of the inks themselves reserved for a few well-chosen highlights. For the rest, green acts as an excellent foil for the rich reds and purples of the central conch shell.

Writing modestly of his own work, Mr. Wilson said, "I have used seashells in a still-life group with the idea that they would make possible an iridescent effect. I think I have been reasonably successful."

It is doubtful that this effect of iridescence could be accomplished more successfully by any other art or printing medium.

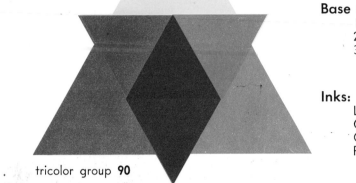

tricolor group **90**

MATCHING KEY

Base colors:			Index
1. process yellow		....	**2**
2. process red		....	**6**
3. royal blue		....	**32**

Inks:	**1.**	**2.**	**3.**
Letterpress —	OP-2	OP-6	OP-32
Offset —	OPO-2	OPO-6	OPO-32
Gravure —	OPG-2	OPG-6	OPG-32
Flexographic —	OPF-2	OPF-6	OPF-32

A. group 90 plus red

B. group 90 plus chrome yellow

C. group 90 plus orange

D. group 90 plus brown

E. group 90 plus gray

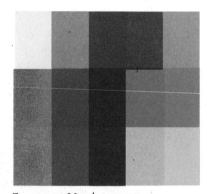

F. group 90 plus green

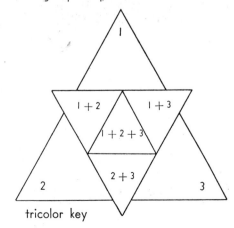

tricolor key

G. group 90 plus purple

H. group 90 plus process blue

MATCHING KEY

Base colors: *Index*
1. process yellow   2
2. green   18
3. purple   20

Inks:	**1.**	**2.**	**3.**
Letterpress	— OP-2	OP-18	OP-20
Offset	— OPO-2	OPO-18	OPO-20
Gravure	— OPG-2	OPG-18	OPG-20
Flexographic	— OPF-2	OPF-18	OPF-20

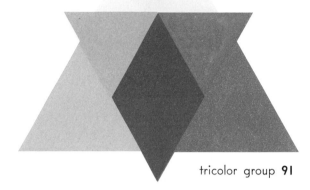

tricolor group **91**

A. group 91 plus red

B. group 91 plus chrome yellow

C. group 91 plus orange

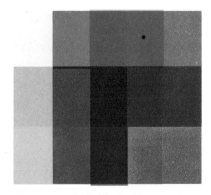

D. group 91 plus process red

E. group 91 plus brown

F. group 91 plus gray

G. group 91 plus royal blue

H. group 91 plus process blue

1	1 + 3	1 + 2 + 3	2 + 3	3
1 + 2	1 + 2 + 4	1 + 2 + 3 + 4	1 + 3 + 4	3 + 4
2	2 + 4	2 + 3 + 4	1 + 4	4

four-color key

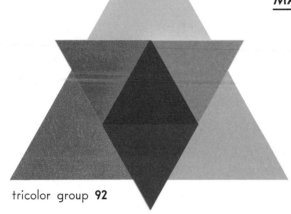

tricolor group **92**

MATCHING KEY

Base colors: *Index*
1. chrome yellow   1
2. process red   6
3. process blue 34

Inks:	**1.**	**2.**	**3.**
Letterpress —	OP-1	OP-6	OP-34
Offset —	OPO-1	OPO-6	OPO-34
Gravure —	OPG-1	OPG-6	OPG-34
Flexographic —	OPF-1	OPF-6	OPF-34

A. group 92 plus red

B. group 92 plus process yellow

C. group 92 plus orange

D. group 92 plus brown

E. group 92 plus gray

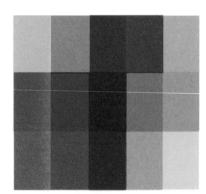

F. group 92 plus green

tricolor key

G. group 92 plus purple

H. group 92 plus royal blue

MATCHING KEY

Base colors:

	Index
1. orange	4
2. gray	17
3. purple	20

Inks:

	1.	2.	3.
Letterpress	OP-4	OP-17	OP-20
Offset	OPO-4	OPO-17	OPO-20
Gravure	OPG-4	OPG-17	OPG-20
Flexographic	OPF-4	OPF-17	OPF-20

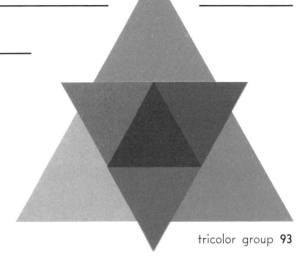

tricolor group **93**

A. group 93 plus red

B. group 93 plus chrome yellow

C. group 93 plus process yellow

D. group 93 plus process red

E. group 93 plus brown

F. group 93 plus green

G. group 93 plus royal blue

H. group 93 plus process blue

1	1 + 3	1 + 2 + 3	2 + 3	3
1 + 2	1 + 2 + 4	1 + 2 + 3 + 4	1 + 3 + 4	3 + 4
2	2 + 4	2 + 3 + 4	1 + 4	4

four-color key

STILL LIFE

Advertising illustration by W. Parke Johnson
Color group 95 plus black
Rendering: Black key, woodcut tools on scratchboard. Color areas, woodcut
        tools on Bourges sheets: 100% Process Yellow, 100% Process Red,
        100% Process Blue. Colors used here are closer to 70% tints.
Process: Letterpress. No reduction.

As proof that the potentialities of solid-color overprinting are virtually unlimited, this illustration should satisfy the most exacting critics. Here in one small but exquisitely wrought drawing is visual evidence that any effect, any texture, any degree of color tonality can be created in line by an artist and reproduced *precisely as he drew it*.

Since this example was rendered actual size, there is no loss whatsoever, either in detail or in color. The overprint is as sharp, as brilliant and as rich in texture as the original art copy. If there are errors, they are the artist's, not mechanical inadequacies of camera or press. If there are rich, subtle tones in the background tapestry, they were put there by the artist, exactly as they appear on the printed page.

As more and more artists develop the skills to execute pictures of this kind, a new technical term of reference will inevitably come into being: "full-color line reproduction." The thoroughly developed four-color overprint is just that, particularly when the standard process colors are used. We might list six principal categories in art reproduction:

halftone	line
duotone	two-color line
full-color halftone	*full-color line*

At last we have filled in the missing category.

to understand that the artist himself made each separation on a Bourges overlay sheet of the color shown here, rendering it in registered position so that he could see the overprint colors as he worked. Facsimile reproduction is the result.

On these facing pages are the four line plates for W. Parke Johnson's *Still Life* overprint. (See illustration facing page 146.) In order to show the exquisite detail of the artist's separations, these plates are reproduced actual size. It is important

shown here. The filters recommended for photographing each of these colors in line are listed on pages 14 and 15. Of particular interest is the perfection of fine detail maintained in the line negative made from a process blue overlay.

For printing by letterpress on coated paper, these line cuts were made as zinc originals, then cast as electrotypes. The art copy consisted of a black and white scratchboard drawing and three transparent color overlays exactly as they are

HANDEL
conducted by
MOGENS WÖLDIKE

TE DEUM *for the Peace of Utrecht*
& Coronation **ANTHEM** *"Let Thy Hand Be Strengthened"*

Ruth Guldbæk, SOPRANO I
Valborg Garde, SOPRANO II
Else Brems, ALTO I
Dagmar Schou, ALTO II
Ole Walbom, TENOR I
Volmer Holbøll, TENOR II
Einar Nørby, BASS
Søren Sørensen, ORGANIST

The Chamber Orchestra of the Danish State Radio   *The Chorus of the Danish State Radio*

Joseph Low

THE HAYDN SOCIETY · Boston   HSL-2046

Artist: Joseph Low
Art Director: Alvin Eisenman
Client: The Haydn Society, Inc.

HANDEL'S TE DEUM

Record cover design by Joseph Low
Tricolor group 95
Rendering: India ink and red showcard color on illustration board.
Process: Letterpress. Reduction, 12¼ to 8½.

In the packaging field, display covers on recordings are outstanding for their adventurous color and design. The percentage of really fine work being done for the major producers of symphonic records is amazingly high, and it is interesting to note that it was one of the first art categories to make frequent use of solid-color over-printing.

Joseph Low's striking designs for Haydn Society productions typify some of the best work done in a field that maintains an exceptionally high level in contemporary art. Although the printed cover suggests a use of overlays, the entire art copy was rendered on a single piece of illustration board, as shown in the small reproduction above. Careful instructions to the engraver were necessary for the achievement of the letterpress overprint at the left. By combining positives and negatives, painting out details in different sections of the various colors, three plates were made from the one drawing. The blue plate, for example, was made from a combined positive and negative of the artwork to achieve the solid blue background and the reverse type in the panels. Some areas, as on the figures, were filled on the blue plate, while the detail was held on the red. What appears at first to be the black type of the title is simply two impressions—red and blue—over the solid yellow panel.

Those parts of the design which were rendered in red on the art copy simply helped to guide the engraver in separating the various elements. The entire drawing could have been made in black to reach the same printed conclusion.

Reprinted from *The Boy Who Stole the Elephant,*
by Julilly Kohler, illustrated by Lee Ames, by permission of Alfred A. Knopf, Inc.

CIRCUS PARADE

Juvenile book endpaper design by Lee Ames
Tricolor group 95 plus black
Rendering: Black areas, brush and India ink on illustration board. Color areas,
           Bourges sheets: 70% Process Yellow, 70% Process Red, 50% Process
           Blue.
Process: Offset. Reduction, 3 to 2.

For gay, colorful subjects such as this, no type of color reproduction could improve upon line overprinting. All the boldness and color of a circus poster are in this bright design for the endpapers of Julilly Kohler's book *The Boy Who Stole the Elephant.*

Despite the fact that the illustrator has furnished a black key, much of the drawing is delineated by unsupported color. In the foreground, figures of watching children are silhouetted; thus black is used as the darkest color in the composition rather than as a mere structural outline. Beyond this shadowy foreground group, the vivid color of the parade itself glitters in sunshine.

This particular example is from a book which, like the Winston Pixie Books, is illustrated throughout by striking overprints. When the artwork for Color by Overprinting was being assembled, *The Boy Who Stole the Elephant* was one of the few books published in the United States which contained this type of color reproduction. Undoubtedly more have appeared since the collection was made, and it is to be hoped that varied selection of color will soon become the rule. Not being under the compulsion of advertising requirements, as are most national magazines, color printing in books need not be restricted to the standard "process" yellow, red and blue.

tricolor group **94**

MATCHING KEY

Base colors: *Index*

1. process red 6
2. gray 17
3. green 18

Inks:

	1.	**2.**	**3.**
Letterpress —	OP-6	OP-17	OP-18
Offset —	OPO-6	OPO-17	OPO-18
Gravure —	OPG-6	OPG-17	OPG-18
Flexographic —	OPF-6	OPF-17	OPF-18

A. group 94 plus red

B. group 94 plus chrome yellow

C. group 94 plus process yellow

D. group 94 plus orange

E. group 94 plus brown

F. group 94 plus purple

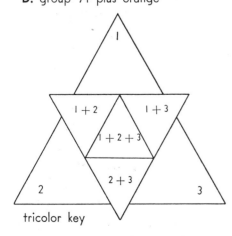

tricolor key

G. group 94 plus royal blue

H. group 94 plus process blue

MATCHING KEY

Base colors: *Index*
1. process yellow **2**
2. process red **6**
3. process blue **34**

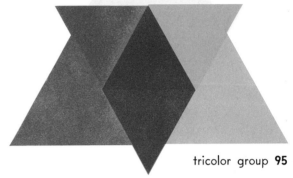

tricolor group **95**

Inks:	1.	2.	3.
Letterpress —	OP-2	OP-6	OP-34
Offset —	OPO-2	OPO-6	OPO-34
Gravure —	OPG-2	OPG-6	OPG-34
Flexographic —	OPF-2	OPF-6	OPF-34

A. group 95 plus red

B. group 95 plus chrome yellow

C. group 95 plus orange

D. group 95 plus brown

E. group 95 plus gray

F. group 95 plus green

G. group 95 plus purple

H. group 95 plus royal blue

1	1 + 3	1 + 2 + 3	2 + 3	3
1 + 2	1 + 2 + 4	1 + 2 + 3 + 4	1 + 3 + 4	3 + 4
2	2 + 4	2 + 3 + 4	1 + 4	4

four-color key

The illustrations on these two pages are not only brilliant examples of solid-color over-printing, but are among the most delightful drawings ever made for Lewis Carroll's classic. They have the same dreamlike whimsicality as the story, and although Huehnergarth's style is highly individual, he has nevertheless maintained much of the traditional concept in his portrayal of principal characters.

A surprising feature of these sparkling pictures is the fact that the color overlays were prepared by a second artist. As John Huehnergarth completed his pen and ink drawings, Edward F. Cortese prepared the overlays. The result is an example of perfect teamwork, since the color effects appear as an integral part of the compositions.

The reproductions in the original edition were by offset, as they are here.

ALICE IN WONDERLAND

Book illustrations by John Huehnergarth
Tricolor group 95 plus black
Rendering: Black key, pen and India ink on illustration board.
    Color areas, plastic stylus on Bourges sheets: 70% Process Yellow; 70% Process Red; 70% Process Blue.
Process: Offset. No reduction.

Although dependent upon the black key for their character, these overprints are enhanced by creative application of color. Notice how some of the fish in the illustration above are only partly delineated by a black line. Also note the varied color balance of the different drawings, achieved with the same three basic process inks.

Illustrations from
the PIXIE BOOK edition of
Alice in Wonderland.
Published by The John C. Winston Company.

tricolor group **96**

MATCHING KEY

Base colors:			Index
1. orange	. . . .		4
2. process red	. . . .		6
3. royal blue	. . . .		32

Inks:	**1.**	**2.**	**3.**
Letterpress —	OP-4	OP-6	OP-32
Offset —	OPO-4	OPO-6	OPO-32
Gravure —	OPG-4	OPG-6	OPG-32
Flexographic —	OPF-4	OPF-6	OPF-32

A. group 96 plus red

B. group 96 plus chrome yellow

C. group 96 plus process yellow

D. group 96 plus brown

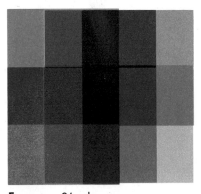

E. group 96 plus gray

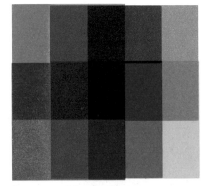

F. group 96 plus green

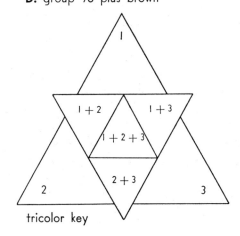

tricolor key

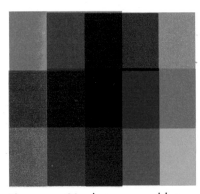

G. group 96 plus purple

H. group 96 plus process blue

CHRISTMAS IN OLD ENGLAND

Greeting card design by Edward F. Cortese
Tricolor group 95 plus black
Rendering: Black key, pen and India ink on illustration board. Color areas, plastic
stylus on Bourges sheets: 70% Process Yellow, 70% Process Red,
50% Process Blue.
Process: Letterpress. Reduction, 3 to 2.

The standard group of process colors (yellow, red and blue) produces the full spectrum, including the secondaries: orange, green and purple. For a great many commercial uses this is the most practical color group, not only because it includes all the basic colors of the spectrum but because a solid-color subject such as this could be run with a full-color halftone illustration. Assuming this were to be done, either the line overprint would have to be reproduced in stronger shades of colors than shown above, or each plate would have to be made with a 70% screen.

Original Photograph   (Courtesy Al Paul Lefton Co., Inc.)   Line Conversion

COUNTRY STORE

Photographic overprint by Donald E. Cooke
Original photograph and line conversion by Peter Dant Photographic Illustrations,
Ardmore, Pa., in conjunction with special techniques developed by the author. *
Tricolor Group 95
Rendering: Stylus on yellow, magenta and blue transparencies of a line print,
    made from a black and white photograph. Some color added with
    pen and acetate ink.
Process: Letterpress. No reduction.

At the left is a three-color line overprint which was derived from an ordinary black and white snapshot. This example, possibly the first of its kind, should suggest infinite applications and variations, since it demonstrates that the overprinting principle is not limited to hand-drawn compositions. It also shows how easily a black and white subject may be converted to a richly colorful picture.

First, a line conversion was made from the original photograph illustrated above. From the line negative, three matrices were made in positive form. These matrices were then treated with yellow, magenta and cyan dyes, providing three color transparencies of the line image—one for each of the process colors.

With the color transparencies mounted in registered position on a white board, certain areas of color were removed from each film, exactly as in the rendering of Bourges art. Line engravings were then made for the accompanying overprint.

This illustration would reproduce well in any daily newspaper. The process has application to virtually any subject, publication, or reproduction process. Color transparencies could be made from a pen and ink, or from a black crayon drawing, instead of from a photograph. For another method of converting a black and white line drawing to a multicolor overprint, see pages 64 and 65.

PITCHER AND FRUIT

Still life by Donald E. Cooke
Tricolor group 95 plus black
Rendering: Specially formulated transparent colored inks on grained acetate
    overlays.
Process: Letterpress. Reduction, 3 to 2.

To the author's knowledge this is the first full-color line overprint ever made by the additive method of applying transparent color to clear overlays. While techniques for this unexplored medium still require mastery by artists, this first experiment suggests many possible applications.

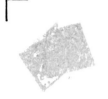

Here is the same illustration reproduced on cellophane with rubber plates and flexographic inks. It was printed on a four-color flexographic press by the Diaphane Corporation, Philadelphia. Detailed information on this type of print is given on the next page. For more about flexographic inks, see page 13.

THE FLEXOGRAPHIC OVERPRINT

AN examination of the prints on the two preceding pages will reveal some marked differences in effect, though they were derived from the same art copy.

The letterpress print on coated paper at the left has a sharp, almost brittle quality, with every minute dot maintaining its individual identity. In this respect it is the more accurate reproduction of the two.

However, the flexographic print on cellophane at the right has a pleasing quality of softness which has artistic merit of its own. Curiously, the *effect* of the flexographic reproduction more closely approximates the soft quality and texture of crayon work.

This paradox might be explained thus: When a crayon is drawn over a rough surface, it leaves deposits of color on the peaks of the surface texture. Magnified, any one of these dots would show variation of tone, being dark in the center and lighter at the outer edges. In line reproduction, the zinc engraving records the color dots only as sharply defined areas. The soft, lighter edges are either lost, or become one with the solid center portion. On the other hand, rubber plates made from the metal engravings are comparatively soft. Also flexographic inks are more fluid than most inks for other processes. As a result, the small dots have a tendency to spread, even under light pressure, and the deposits of ink are less sharply defined. It is because of these factors that fine-screen halftones are difficult to print by the flexographic process and line plates, quite naturally, dominate the field.

When flexography has been selected as the process for color by overprinting it is important to bear in mind that standard procedures which have governed this process for years are completely applicable to the principles of solid-color overprinting. On transparent flex-ible films such as cellophane and polyethylene, an opaque white must be applied in order to lend opacity to the print. Standard, fully pigmented inks are satisfactory, provided they are transparent enough to allow the underlay colors to show through.

Transparency of colors may dictate the sequence in which they will be applied. Yellow and orange will usually be first-down colors because of their opacity, while the more transparent reds and blues will generally follow. In all cases black should be last. When reverse printing (on the "back" of the film) is used, the sequence must be inverted.

In overprinting on cellophane by flexography, the same distance between colors, oven and chill-roll temperatures, and ink dilution ratios are recommended as for regular cellophane and polyethylene printing. Other transparent flexible film should be printed in the same general manner, with inks recommended for those specific materials.

On paper, white is needed as a first-down color only when it is desirable to mask the tint of the printing surface, as in the case of brown kraft. Since strong transparent dyes are used in the ink formulation there is less restriction in the color sequence on paper than there is on film.

Flexographic plates are usually made from standard metal letterpress engravings, such as deeply etched zinc or copper. First a negative plastic mold is made from the engraving. Into this a soft, gummy rubber, or "raw stock" is molded under pressure and heat. The vulcanizing process produces a semihard rubber plate. Hardness of the plate can be controlled, and may range from 45 to 65 Durometer, depending on printing requirements. Soft plates will carry more ink than hard ones and will conform better to a rough printing surface.

MATCHING KEY

Base colors: *Index*
1. orange **4**
2. green **18**
3. purple **20**

Inks: **1.**   **2.**   **3.**

	1.	2.	3.
Letterpress	OP-4	OP-18	OP-20
Offset	OPO-4	OPO-18	OPO-20
Gravure	OPG-4	OPG-18	OPG-20
Flexographic	OPF-4	OPF-18	OPF-20

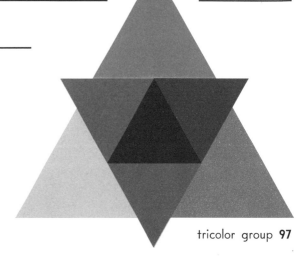

tricolor group **97**

A. group 97 plus red

B. group 97 plus chrome yellow

C. group 97 plus process yellow

D. group 97 plus process red

E. group 97 plus brown

F. group 97 plus gray

G. group 97 plus royal blue

H. group 97 plus process blue

1	1 + 3	1 + 2 + 3	2 + 3	3
1 + 2	1 + 2 + 4	1 + 2 + 3 + 4	1 + 3 + 4	3 + 4
2	2 + 4	2 + 3 + 4	1 + 4	4

four-color key

tricolor group **98**

MATCHING KEY

Base colors:		Index
1. process red	....	6
2. gray	....	17
3. purple	....	20

Inks:	**1.**	**2.**	**3.**
Letterpress —	OP-6	OP-17	OP-20
Offset —	OPO-6	OPO-17	OPO-20
Gravure —	OPG-6	OPG-17	OPG-20
Flexographic —	OPF-6	OPF-17	OPF-20

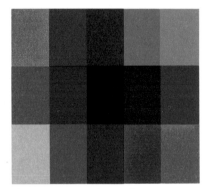

A. group 98 plus red

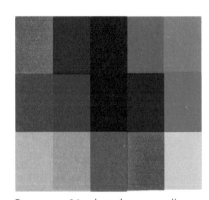

B. group 98 plus chrome yellow

C. group 98 plus process yellow

D. group 98 plus orange

E. group 98 plus brown

F. group 98 plus green

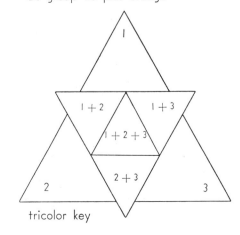

tricolor key

G. group 98 plus royal blue

H. group 98 plus process blue

MATCHING KEY

Base colors: *Index*
1. red 0
2. brown 12
3. royal blue 32

Inks: **1.**   **2.**   **3.**

	1.	**2.**	**3.**
Letterpress —	OP-0	OP-12	OP-32
Offset —	OPO-0	OPO-12	OPO-32
Gravure —	OPG-0	OPG-12	OPG-32
Flexographic —	OPF-0	OPF-12	OPF-32

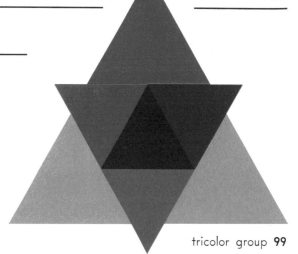

tricolor group **99**

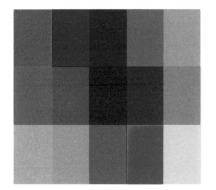

A. group 99 plus chrome yellow

B. group 99 plus process yellow

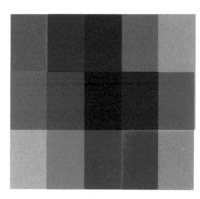

C. group 99 plus orange

D. group 99 plus process red

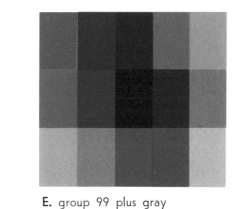

E. group 99 plus gray

F. group 99 plus green

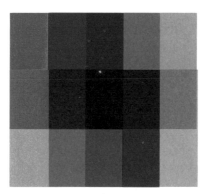

G. group 99 plus purple

H. group 99 plus process blue

1	1 + 3	1 + 2 + 3	2 + 3	3
1 + 2	1 + 2 + 4	1 + 2 + 3 + 4	1 + 3 + 4	3 + 4
2	2 + 4	2 + 3 + 4	1 + 4	4

four-color key

tricolor group **100**

MATCHING KEY

Base colors: *Index*
1. orange **4**
2. process red **6**
3. process blue **34**

Inks: **1.**   **2.**   **3.**

	1.	2.	3.
Letterpress —	OP-4	OP-6	OP-34
Offset —	OPO-4	OPO-6	OPO-34
Gravure —	OPG-4	OPG-6	OPG-34
Flexographic —	OPF-4	OPF-6	OPF-34

A. group 100 plus red

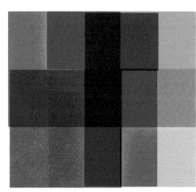

B. group 100 plus chrome yellow

C. group 100 plus process yellow

D. group 100 plus brown

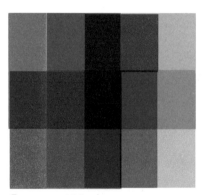

E. group 100 plus gray

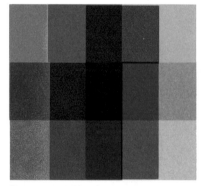

F. group 100 plus green

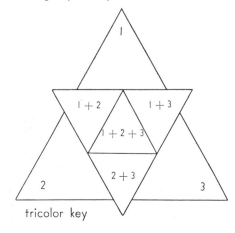

tricolor key

G. group 100 plus purple

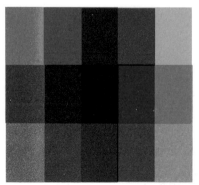

H. group 100 plus royal blue

MATCHING KEY

Base colors: *Index*
1. process red 6
2. green 18
3. purple 20

Inks:

	1.	2.	3.
Letterpress	OP-6	OP-18	OP-20
Offset	OPO-6	OPO-18	OPO-20
Gravure	OPG-6	OPG-18	OPG-20
Flexographic	OPF-6	OPF-18	OPF-20

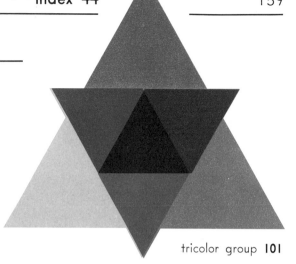

tricolor group **101**

A. group 101 plus red

B. group 101 plus chrome yellow

C. group 101 plus process yellow

D. group 101 plus orange

E. group 101 plus brown

F. group 101 plus gray

G. group 101 plus royal blue

H. group 101 plus process blue

1	1 + 3	1 + 2 + 3	2 + 3	3
1 + 2	1 + 2 + 4	1 + 2 + 3 + 4	1 + 3 + 4	3 + 4
2	2 + 4	2 + 3 + 4	1 + 4	4

four-color key

tricolor group **102**

MATCHING KEY

Base colors: *Index*
1. chrome yellow 1
2. brown 12
3. royal blue 32

Inks:	**1.**	**2.**	**3.**
Letterpress —	OP-1	OP-12	OP-32
Offset —	OPO-1	OPO-12	OPO-32
Gravure —	OPG-1	OPG-12	OPG-32
Flexographic —	OPF-1	OPF-12	OPF-32

A. group 102 plus red

B. group 102 plus process yellow

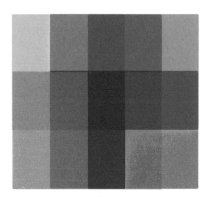

C. group 102 plus orange

D. group 102 plus process red

E. group 102 plus gray

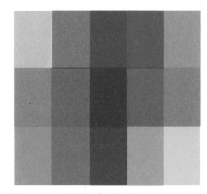

F. group 102 plus green

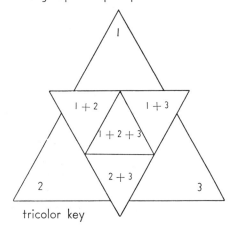

tricolor key

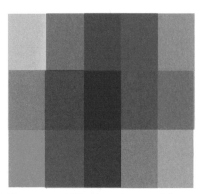

G. group 102 plus purple

H. group 102 plus process blue

INTERMEDIATE GROUPS

index 46 to 55

This section of the color charts takes in a range of ten index figures, from 46 to 55, and is made up largely of well-balanced tricolor groups. Included are many groups containing at least one of the two intermediate, or neutral, colors themselves: gray and brown. It will also be noticed that a number of the intermediate groups contain complementary colors, such as orange and blue, or red and green, whose overprints may also be placed in the neutral category.

MATCHING KEY

Base colors: *Index*
1. red 0
2. brown 12
3. process blue 34

Inks:

	1.	**2.**	**3.**
Letterpress —	OP-0	OP-12	OP-34
Offset —	OPO-0	OPO-12	OPO-34
Gravure —	OPG-0	OPG-12	OPG-34
Flexographic —	OPF-0	OPF-12	OPF-34

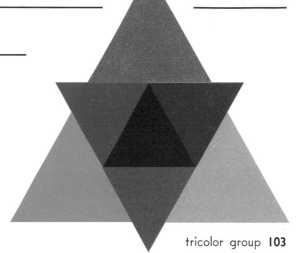

tricolor group **103**

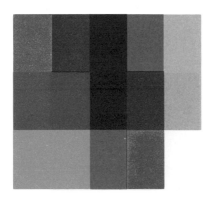

A. group 103 plus chrome yellow

B. group 103 plus process yellow

C. group 103 plus orange

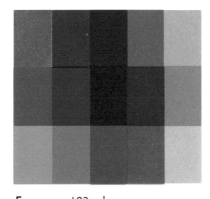

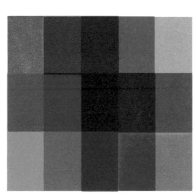

D. group 103 plus process red

E. group 103 plus gray

F. group 103 plus green

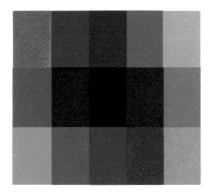

G. group 103 plus purple

H. group 103 plus royal blue

1	1 + 3	1 + 2 + 3	2 + 3	3
1 + 2	1 + 2 + 4	1 + 2 + 3 + 4	1 + 3 + 4	3 + 4
2	2 + 4	2 + 3 + 4	1 + 4	4

four-color key

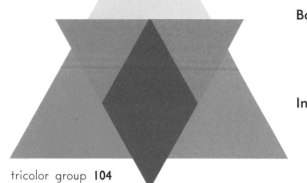

tricolor group **104**

MATCHING KEY

Base colors: *Index*
1. process yellow **2**
2. brown **12**
3. royal blue **32**

Inks: **1.**   **2.**   **3.**
Letterpress — OP-2   OP-12   OP-32
Offset   — OPO-2   OPO-12   OPO-32
Gravure   — OPG-2   OPG-12   OPG-32
Flexographic — OPF-2   OPF-12   OPF-32

A. group 104 plus red

B. group 104 plus chrome yellow

C. group 104 plus orange

D. group 104 plus process red

E. group 104 plus gray

F. group 104 plus green

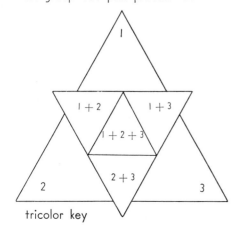

tricolor key

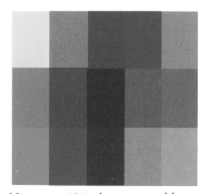

G. group 104 plus purple   **H.** group 104 plus process blue

MATCHING KEY

Base colors: *Index*
    1. chrome yellow   1
    2. brown 12
    3. process blue **34**

Inks:

	1.	2.	3.
Letterpress	— OP-1	OP-12	OP-34
Offset	— OPO-1	OPO-12	OPO-34
Gravure	— OPG-1	OPG-12	OPG-34
Flexographic	— OPF-1	OPF-12	OPF-34

tricolor group **105**

A. group 105 plus red

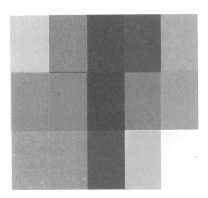

B. group 105 plus process yellow

C. group 105 plus orange

D. group 105 plus process red

E. group 105 plus gray

F. group 105 plus green

G. group 105 plus purple

H. group 105 plus royal blue

1	1 + 3	1 + 2 + 3	2 + 3	3
1 + 2	1 + 2 + 4	1 + 2 + 3 + 4	1 + 3 + 4	3 + 4
2	2 + 4	2 + 3 + 4	1 + 4	4

four-color key

IN THE RUINS

Symbolic illustration by Harve Stein
Tricolor group 107 plus black
Rendering: Black key, brush and India ink on illustration board. Color areas,
plastic stylus on Bourges sheets: 70% Process Yellow, 50% Brown,
50% Process Blue.
Process: Offset. Reduction, 4 to 3.

A fine example of what can be done with Bourges overlays to create design through representational form, this skilfully rendered overprint is hard to classify. It could serve effectively as a magazine illustration, book illustration, or art print. Actually it was done for its own sake and therefore should probably be placed in the last of the three categories.

At the same time, it suggests what might be done by progressive illustrators and art directors in the "slick" magazine field. Since overlays of transparent color represent a strictly contemporary art medium, the development of a new contemporary school of magazine illustration may very well begin with this kind of solid-color overprinting. (See also the illustrations on pages 79 and 181.)

Mr. Stein, a prominent illustrator and an instructor at the Rhode Island School of Design, writes: "Because this is a new reproduction process I felt that my approach should be in that direction, with interpenetrations of form and a strong accent on textures. . . . Incidentally, this is a marvelous medium for achieving painting effects."

It is significant to hear artists talking about painting effects in a solid-color medium. Actually, every stroke which removes color pigment from transparent overlay sheets has the effect of painting with colored light, since the subtraction of pigment results in the addition of light vibrations. It is this unique feature of overprinting which gives it a luminosity unmatched by any other kind of art print.

tricolor group **106**

MATCHING KEY

Base colors:			*Index*
1. brown	....		**12**
2. gray	....		**17**
3. green	....		**18**

Inks:	**1.**	**2.**	**3.**
Letterpress —	OP-12	OP-17	OP-18
Offset —	OPO-12	OPO-17	OPO-18
Gravure —	OPG-12	OPG-17	OPG-18
Flexographic —	OPF-12	OPF-17	OPF-18

A. group 106 plus red

B. group 106 plus chrome yellow

C. group 106 plus process yellow

D. group 106 plus orange

E. group 106 plus process red

F. group 106 plus purple

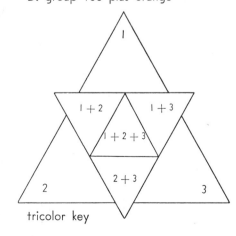

tricolor key

G. group 106 plus royal blue

H. group 106 plus process blue

MATCHING KEY

Base colors: *Index*
     1. process yellow **2**
     2. brown **12**
     3. process blue **34**

Inks: **I.**   **2.**   **3.**
   Letterpress — OP-2   OP-12   OP-34
   Offset   — OPO-2   OPO-12   OPO-34
   Gravure   — OPG-2   OPG-12   OPG-34
   Flexographic — OPF-2   OPF-12   OPF-34

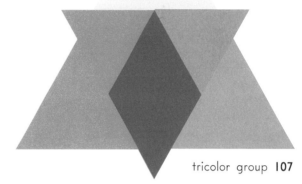

tricolor group **107**

A. group 107 plus red

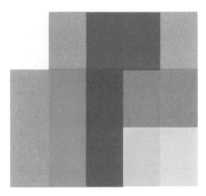

B. group 107 plus chrome yellow

C. group 107 plus orange

D. group 107 plus process red

E. group 107 plus gray

F. group 107 plus green

G. group 107 plus purple

H. group 107 plus royal blue

1	1 + 3	1 + 2 + 3	2 + 3	3
1 + 2	1 + 2 + 4	1 + 2 + 3 + 4	1 + 3 + 4	3 + 4
2	2 + 4	2 + 3 + 4	1 + 4	4

four-color key

OLD MAN OF THE SEA

Portrait by Edward F. Cortese
Color group 106D (also groups 60E, 63E, 87E)
Rendering: Plastic stylus on Bourges sheets: 100% Orange, 50% Brown, 70%
Green, 50% Black.
Process: Offset. No reduction.

A superb example of detail combined with the simplicity of bold poster technique. In this case the gray plate carries most of the detailed delineation of facial lines, while the other three plates are limited to large masses of solid color. The result is a startling character study.

After completing the picture, the artist found that the eyes lacked depth, as he had removed all green from the facial area. In order to restore the dark shadows he needed, he cut a small strip of green adhesive Bourges material large enough to cover the eyes, and attached it to the green overlay. He then reworked this area, removing all color except in the shadows directly under the eyebrows. The final darks thus attained help to give the portrait its arresting power.

Such corrections can easily be made, and since the patchwork does not show in the printed illustration, nothing is lost. It should be borne in mind, too, that an entire overlay can be replaced and redone if, through some accident, it is too seriously marred for correction. In this event, only one-fourth of the work must be done over, whereas if an accident occurs in the rendering of a water color, for example, the entire picture may be lost.

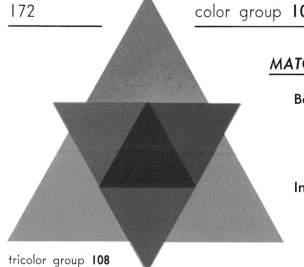

tricolor group **108**

MATCHING KEY

Base colors: *Index*
  1. orange **4**
  2. brown **12**
  3. royal blue **32**

Inks:	**1.**	**2.**	**3.**
Letterpress —	OP-4	OP-12	OP-32
Offset —	OPO-4	OPO-12	OPO-32
Gravure —	OPG-4	OPG-12	OPG-32
Flexographic —	OPF-4	OPF-12	OPF-32

A. group 108 plus red

B. group 108 plus chrome yellow

C. group 108 plus process yellow

D. group 108 plus process red

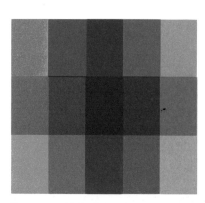

E. group 108 plus gray

F. group 108 plus green

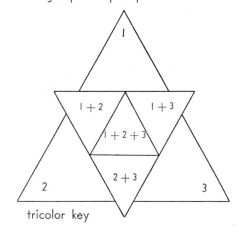

tricolor key

G. group 108 plus purple

H. group 108 plus process blue

MATCHING KEY

Base colors: *Index*
1. red **0**
2. gray **17**
3. royal blue **32**

Inks:	**1.**	**2.**	**3.**
Letterpress —	OP-0	OP-17	OP-32
Offset —	OPO-0	OPO-17	OPO-32
Gravure —	OPG-0	OPG-17	OPG-32
Flexographic —	OPF-0	OPF-17	OPF-32

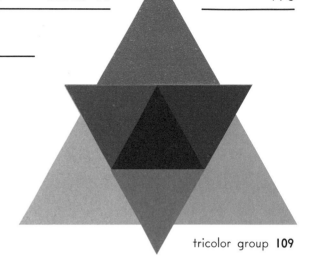

tricolor group **109**

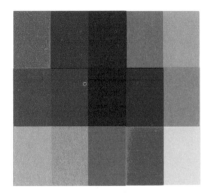

A. group 109 plus chrome yellow

B. group 109 plus process yellow

C. group 109 plus orange

D. group 109 plus process red

E. group 109 plus brown

F. group 109 plus green

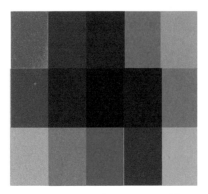

G. group 109 plus purple

H. group 109 plus process blue

1	1 + 3	1 + 2 + 3	2 + 3	3
1 + 2	1 + 2 + 4	1 + 2 + 3 + 4	1 + 3 + 4	3 + 4
2	2 + 4	2 + 3 + 4	1 + 4	4

four-color key

tricolor group **110**

MATCHING KEY

Base colors:			Index
1. brown	....		12
2. gray	....		17
3. purple			20

Inks:	1.	2.	3.
Letterpress —	OP-12	OP-17	OP-20
Offset —	OPO-12	OPO-17	OPO-20
Gravure —	OPG-12	OPG-17	OPG-20
Flexographic —	OPF-12	OPF-17	OPF-20

A. group 110 plus red

B. group 110 plus chrome yellow

C. group 110 plus process yellow

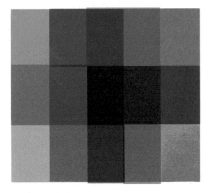

D. group 110 plus orange

E. group 110 plus process red

F. group 110 plus green

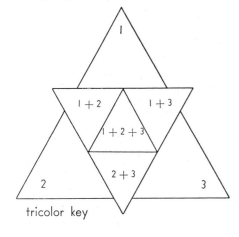

tricolor key

G. group 110 plus royal blue

H. group 110 plus process blue

MATCHING KEY

Base colors: *Index*
     1. red 0
     2. green 18
     3. royal blue 32

Inks:	1.	2.	3.
Letterpress —	OP-0	OP-18	OP-32
Offset —	OPO-0	OPO-18	OPO-32
Gravure —	OPG-0	OPG-18	OPG-32
Flexographic —	OPF-0	OPF-18	OPF-32

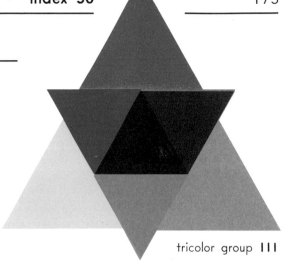

tricolor group III

A. group III plus chrome yellow

B. group III plus process yellow

C. group III plus orange

D. group III plus process red

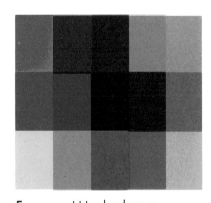

E. group III plus brown

F. group III plus gray

G. group III plus purple

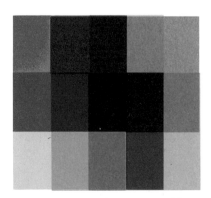

H. group III plus process blue

1	1 + 3	1 + 2 + 3	2 + 3	3
1 + 2	1 + 2 + 4	1 + 2 + 3 + 4	1 + 3 + 4	3 + 4
2	2 + 4	2 + 3 + 4	1 + 4	4

four-color key

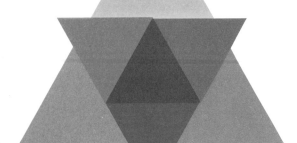

tricolor group 112

MATCHING KEY

Base colors: *Index*
  1. chrome yellow   1
  2. gray   17
  3. royal blue   32

Inks:	1.	2.	3.
Letterpress —	OP-1	OP-17	OP-32
Offset —	OPO-1	OPO-17	OPO-32
Gravure —	OPG-1	OPG-17	OPG-32
Flexographic —	OPF-1	OPF-17	OPF-32

A. group 112 plus red

B. group 112 plus process yellow

C. group 112 plus orange

D. group 112 plus process red

E. group 112 plus brown

F. group 112 plus green

tricolor key

G. group 112 plus purple

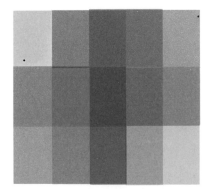

H. group 112 plus process blue

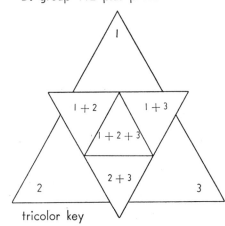

MATCHING KEY

Base colors: *Index*
1. orange **4**
2. brown **12**
3. process blue **34**

Inks:

	1.	2.	3.
Letterpress	OP-4	OP-12	OP-34
Offset	OPO-4	OPO-12	OPO-34
Gravure	OPG-4	OPG-12	OPG-34
Flexographic	OPF-4	OPF-12	OPF-34

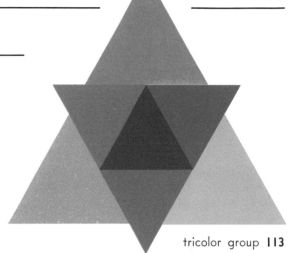

tricolor group **113**

A. group 113 plus red

B. group 113 plus chrome yellow

C. group 113 plus process yellow

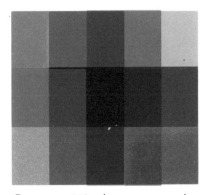

D. group 113 plus process red

E. group 113 plus gray

F. group 113 plus green

G. group 113 plus purple

H. group 113 plus royal blue

1	1 + 3	1 + 2 + 3	2 + 3	3
1 + 2	1 + 2 + 4	1 + 2 + 3 + 4	1 + 3 + 4	3 + 4
2	2 + 4	2 + 3 + 4	1 + 4	4

four-color key

tricolor group 114

MATCHING KEY

Base colors: *Index*
1. process red **6**
2. brown **12**
3. royal blue **32**

Inks:	1.	2.	3.
Letterpress —	OP-6	OP-12	OP-32
Offset —	OPO-6	OPO-12	OPO-32
Gravure —	OPG-6	OPG-12	OPG-32
Flexographic —	OPF-6	OPF-12	OPF-32

A. group 114 plus red

B. group 114 plus chrome yellow

C. group 114 plus process yellow

D. group 114 plus orange

E. group 114 plus gray

F. group 114 plus green

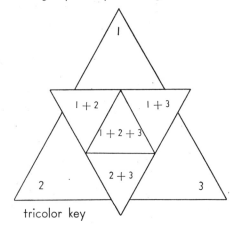

tricolor key

1
1 + 2   1 + 3
1 + 2 + 3
2   2 + 3   3

G. group 114 plus purple

H. group 114 plus process blue

MATCHING KEY

Base colors: *Index*
 1. brown **12**
 2. green **18**
 3. purple **20**

Inks:	**1.**	**2.**	**3.**
Letterpress	OP-12	OP-18	OP-20
Offset	OPO-12	OPO-18	OPO-20
Gravure	OPG-12	OPG-18	OPG-20
Flexographic	OPF-12	OPF-18	OPF-20

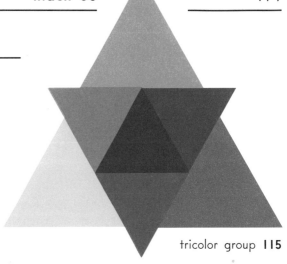

tricolor group **115**

A. group 115 plus red

B. group 115 plus chrome yellow

C. group 115 plus process yellow

D. group 115 plus orange

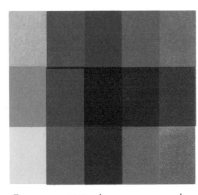

E. group 115 plus process red

F. group 115 plus gray

G. group 115 plus royal blue

H. group 115 plus process blue

1	1 + 3	1 + 2 + 3	2 + 3	3
1 + 2	1 + 2 + 4	1 + 2 + 3 + 4	1 + 3 + 4	3 + 4
2	2 + 4	2 + 3 + 4	1 + 4	4

four-color key

THE WHITE AND THE GOLD
Magazine illustration by Franklin Arbuckle
Tricolor group 114 plus black
Rendering: Black key, lithograph pencil combined with pen and ink. Color areas, stylus on Bourges sheets: 50% Brown, 70% Process Red, 70% Poster Blue.
Process: Offset. Reduction, 5 to 3.

Comparable to a popular U.S. weekly, *Maclean's* Magazine of Canada deserves credit for being one of the first periodicals in this category to use solid-color overprinting.

The illustration shown here is one of a fine series for Thomas B. Costain's *The White and the Gold,* which ran in several issues of *Maclean's* in the spring of 1954. In the magazine itself, the letterpress reproduction was made for coated paper with a halftone key, two line plates (for the brown and red), and a screened tint for the blue.

Here the same artwork is reproduced entirely in line. Although some small detail may have been lost in the black line plate, most areas are enhanced by added sharpness and clarity. Since the supporting color follows the main outlines of the composition, no loss in the black plate is noticeable. The blue used here has the greater clarity of solid color, which cannot be matched by screening an ink of deeper intensity.

Franklin Arbuckle has made excellent use of his medium by restricting black to the figures and to the foreground objects, rendering the chandeliers on only two of the color overlays. As a result, the less important fixtures hold their place nicely.

Illustration by Franklin Arbuckle
for *Maclean's* Magazine.
Art Director, Gene Aliman.
Used by permission of the publisher.

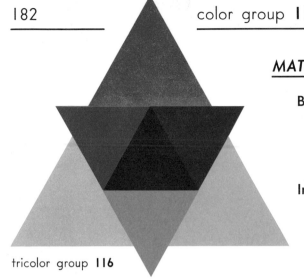

tricolor group **116**

MATCHING KEY

Base colors:		*Index*	
1. red	....	**0**	
2. gray	....	**17**	
3. process blue	....	**34**	

Inks:	**1.**	**2.**	**3.**
Letterpress —	OP-0	OP-17	OP-34
Offset —	OPO-0	OPO-17	OPO-34
Gravure —	OPG-0	OPG-17	OPG-34
Flexographic —	OPF-0	OPF-17	OPF-34

A. group 116 plus chrome yellow

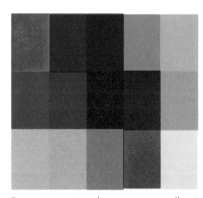

B. group 116 plus process yellow

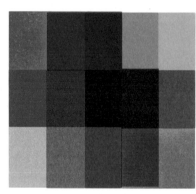

C. group 116 plus orange

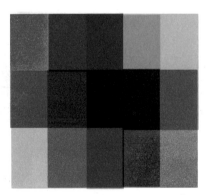

D. group 116 plus process red

E. group 116 plus brown

F. group 116 plus green

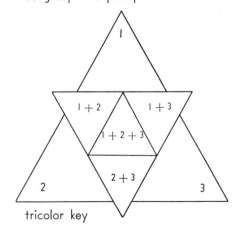

tricolor key

G. group 116 plus purple

H. group 116 plus royal blue

MATCHING KEY

Base colors: *Index*
    1. chrome yellow 1
    2. green **18**
    3. royal blue **32**

Inks: **1.**   **2.**   **3.**
    Letterpress — OP-1   OP-18   OP-32
    Offset   — OPO-1   OPO-18   OPO-32
    Gravure   — OPG-1   OPG-18   OPG-32
    Flexographic— OPF-1   OPF-18   OPF-32

tricolor group **117**

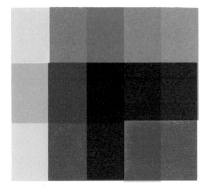

A. group 117 plus red

B. group 117 plus process yellow

C. group 117 plus orange

D. group 117 plus process red

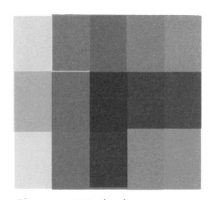

E. group 117 plus brown

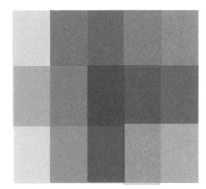

F. group 117 plus gray

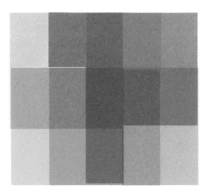

G. group 117 plus purple

H. group 117 plus process blue

1	1 + 3	1 + 2 + 3	2 + 3	3
1 + 2	1 + 2 + 4	1 + 2 + 3 + 4	1 + 3 + 4	3 + 4
2	2 + 4	2 + 3 + 4	1 + 4	4

four-color key

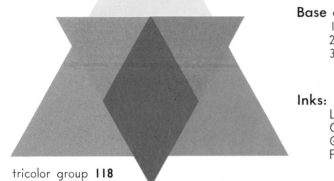

tricolor group **118**

MATCHING KEY

Base colors: *Index*
1. process yellow **2**
2. gray **17**
3. royal blue **32**

Inks:	**1.**	**2.**	**3.**
Letterpress —	OP-2	OP-17	OP-32
Offset —	OPO-2	OPO-17	OPO-32
Gravure —	OPG-2	OPG-17	OPG-32
Flexographic —	OPF-2	OPF-17	OPF-32

A. group 118 plus red

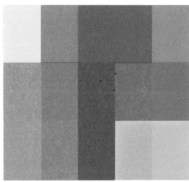

B. group 118 plus chrome yellow

C. group 118 plus orange

D. group 118 plus process red

E. group 118 plus brown

F. group 118 plus green

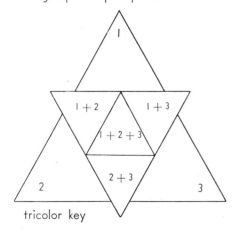

tricolor key

G. group 118 plus purple

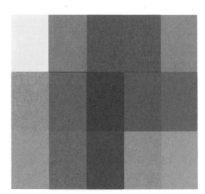

H. group 118 plus process blue

MATCHING KEY

Base colors: *Index*
1. red **0**
2. green **18**
3. process blue **34**

Inks: **I.**   **2.**   **3.**
Letterpress — OP-0   OP-18   OP-34
Offset — OPO-0   OPO-18   OPO-34
Gravure — OPG-0   OPG-18   OPG-34
Flexographic — OPF-0   OPF-18   OPF-34

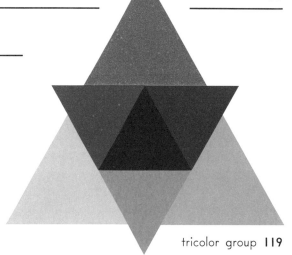

tricolor group **119**

A. group 119 plus chrome yellow

B. group 119 plus process yellow

C. group 119 plus orange

D. group 119 plus process red

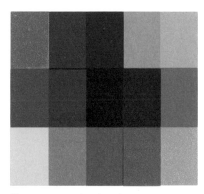

E. group 119 plus brown

F. group 119 plus gray

G. group 119 plus purple

H. group 119 plus royal blue

1	1 + 3	1 + 2 + 3	2 + 3	3
1 + 2	1 + 2 + 4	1 + 2 + 3 + 4	1 + 3 + 4	3 + 4
2	2 + 4	2 + 3 + 4	1 + 4	4

four-color key

PHILADELPHIA WATERFRONT

Industrial landscape by Donald E. Cooke
Tricolor group 118E (also groups 55G, 104E, 145C)
Rendering: Plastic stylus on Bourges sheets: 70% Process Yellow, 50% Brown,
          70% Poster Blue, 50% Black.
Process: Offset. No reduction.

A paintinglike quality may be achieved in an overprint by a judicious selection of color. Any group of the more subtle tints, which combine in close harmony, provides a softness not generally associated with line techniques. In the illustration opposite, the one brilliant color is yellow, which is used sparingly. Only at the immediate center of interest and for some splashes in the foreground is pure process yellow permitted to show.

This device of injecting a few small patches of bright color in an otherwise subdued composition is always effective, and it tends to increase the power and brilliance of color through contrast. Just as a white spot in a black field provides maximum light and shade contrast, so does a patch of brilliant color against a gray or somber-hued background give maximum contrast of color. Many artists, and more buyers of artwork, do not seem to realize that loading a picture or design with violent reds, yellows, blues and greens, all of approximately equal area, may result in an overall impression of dullness, since each color has a tendency to fight for attention, thus destroying the effectiveness of the others.

tricolor group **120**

MATCHING KEY

Base colors: *Index*
1. red **0**
2. purple **20**
3. royal blue **32**

Inks:	1.	2.	3.
Letterpress —	OP-0	OP-20	OP-32
Offset —	OPO-0	OPO-20	OPO-32
Gravure —	OPG-0	OPG-20	OPG-32
Flexographic —	OPF-0	OPF-20	OPF-32

A. group 120 plus chrome yellow

B. group 120 plus process yellow

C. group 120 plus orange

D. group 120 plus process red

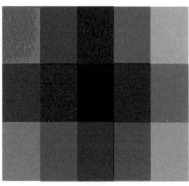

E. group 120 plus brown

F. group 120 plus gray

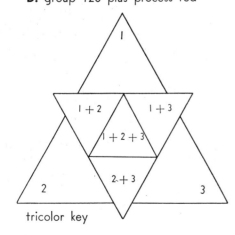

tricolor key

G. group 120 plus green

H. group 120 plus process blue

MATCHING KEY

Base colors: *Index*
1. chrome yellow   1
2. gray   17
3. process blue **34**

Inks:	**1.**	**2.**	**3.**
Letterpress	— OP-1	OP-17	OP-34
Offset	— OPO-1	OPO-17	OPO-34
Gravure	— OPG-1	OPG-17	OPG-34
Flexographic	— OPF-1	OPF-17	OPF-34

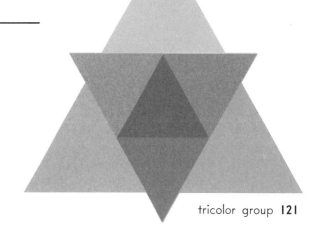

tricolor group **121**

A. group 121 plus red

B. group 121 plus process yellow

C. group 121 plus orange

D. group 121 plus process red

E. group 121 plus brown

F. group 121 plus green

G. group 121 plus purple

H. group 121 plus royal blue

1	1 + 3	1 + 2 + 3	2 + 3	3
1 + 2	1 + 2 + 4	1 + 2 + 3 + 4	1 + 3 + 4	3 + 4
2	2 + 4	2 + 3 + 4	1 + 4	4

four-color key

tricolor group **122**

MATCHING KEY

Base colors: *Index*
  1. process yellow **2**
  2. green **18**
  3. royal blue **32**

Inks:	**1.**	**2.**	**3.**
Letterpress —	OP-2	OP-18	OP-32
Offset —	OPO-2	OPO-18	OPO-32
Gravure —	OPG-2	OPG-18	OPG-32
Flexographic —	OPF-2	OPF-18	OPF-32

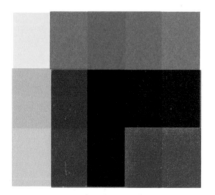

A. group 122 plus red

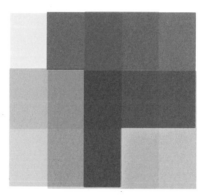

B. group 122 plus chrome yellow

C. group 122 plus orange

D. group 122 plus process red

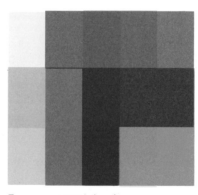

E. group 122 plus brown

F. group 122 plus gray

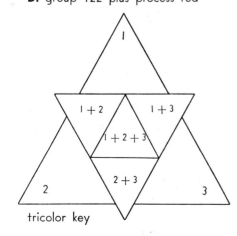

tricolor key

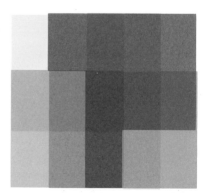

G. group 122 plus purple

H. group 122 plus process blue

MATCHING KEY

Base colors: *Index*
1. process red **6**
2. brown **12**
3. process blue **34**

Inks: **1.**   **2.**   **3.**

	1.	2.	3.
Letterpress	OP-6	OP-12	OP-34
Offset	OPO-6	OPO-12	OPO-34
Gravure	OPG-6	OPG-12	OPG-34
Flexographic	OPF-6	OPF-12	OPF-34

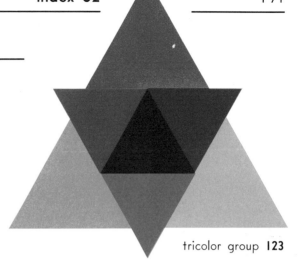

tricolor group **123**

A. group 123 plus red

B. group 123 plus chrome yellow

C. group 123 plus process yellow

D. group 123 plus orange

E. group 123 plus gray

F. group 123 plus green

G. group 123 plus purple

H. group 123 plus royal blue

1	1 + 3	1 + 2 + 3	2 + 3	3
1 + 2	1 + 2 + 4	1 + 2 + 3 + 4	1 + 3 + 4	3 + 4
2	2 + 4	2 + 3 + 4	1 + 4	4

four-color key

tricolor group **124**

MATCHING KEY

Base colors: *Index*
1. chrome yellow 1
2. green 18
3. process blue 34

Inks:	1.	2.	3.
Letterpress —	OP-1	OP-18	OP-34
Offset —	OPO-1	OPO-18	OPO-34
Gravure —	OPG-1	OPG-18	OPG-34
Flexographic —	OPF-1	OPF-18	OPF-34

A. group 124 plus red

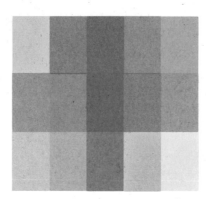

B. group 124 plus process yellow

C. group 124 plus orange

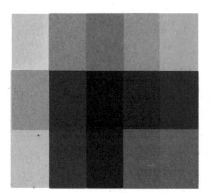

D. group 124 plus process red

E. group 124 plus brown

F. group 124 plus gray

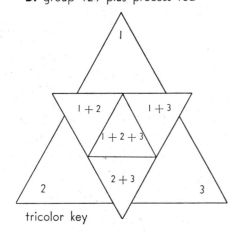

tricolor key

G. group 124 plus purple

H. group 124 plus royal blue

MATCHING KEY

Base colors: *Index*
1. chrome yellow   1
2. purple   20
3. royal blue   32

Inks: **1.**   **2.**   **3.**
Letterpress — OP-1   OP-20   OP-32
Offset   — OPO-1   OPO-20   OPO-32
Gravure   — OPG-1   OPG-20   OPG-32
Flexographic — OPF-1   OPF-20   OPF-32

tricolor group **125**

A. group 125 plus red

B. group 125 plus process yellow

C. group 125 plus orange

D. group 125 plus process red

E. group 125 plus brown

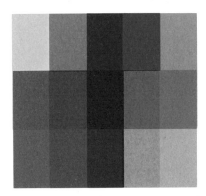

F. group 125 plus gray

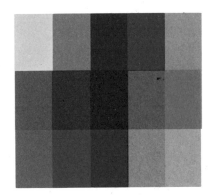

G. group 125 plus green

H. group 125 plus process blue

1	1 + 3	1 + 2 + 3	2 + 3	3
1 + 2	1 + 2 + 4	1 + 2 + 3 + 4	1 + 3 + 4	3 + 4
2	2 + 4	2 + 3 + 4	1 + 4	4

four-color key

tricolor group **126**

MATCHING KEY

Base colors: *Index*
1. process yellow **2**
2. gray **17**
3. process blue **34**

Inks: | **1.** | **2.** | **3.**
|---|---|---|
Letterpress — OP-2 | OP-17 | OP-34
Offset — OPO-2 | OPO-17 | OPO-34
Gravure — OPG-2 | OPG-17 | OPG-34
Flexographic — OPF-2 | OPF-17 | OPF-34

A. group 126 plus red

B. group 126 plus chrome yellow

C. group 126 plus orange

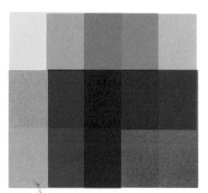

D. group 126 plus process red

E. group 126 plus brown

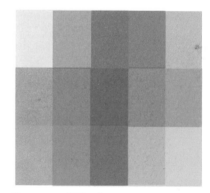

F. group 126 plus green

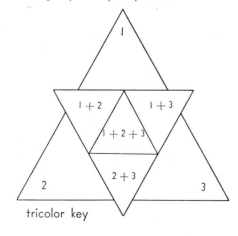

tricolor key

G. group 126 plus purple

H. group 126 plus royal blue

MATCHING KEY

Base colors: *Index*
1. orange **4**
2. gray **17**
3. royal blue **32**

Inks: **1.**   **2.**   **3.**
Letterpress — OP-4   OP-17   OP-32
Offset   — OPO-4   OPO-17   OPO-32
Gravure   — OPG-4   OPG-17   OPG-32
Flexographic — OPF-4   OPF-17   OPF-32

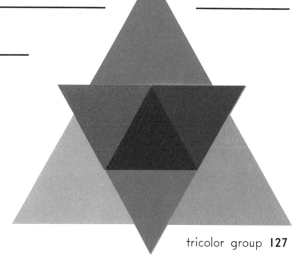

tricolor group **127**

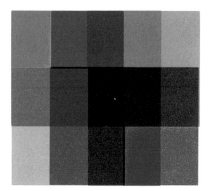

A. group 127 plus red

B. group 127 plus chrome yellow

C. group 127 plus process yellow

D. group 127 plus process red

E. group 127 plus brown

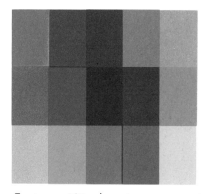

F. group 127 plus green

G. group 127 plus purple

H. group 127 plus process blue

1	1 + 3	1 + 2 + 3	2 + 3	3
1 + 2	1 + 2 + 4	1 + 2 + 3 + 4	1 + 3 + 4	3 + 4
2	2 + 4	2 + 3 + 4	1 + 4	4

four-color key

tricolor group **128**

MATCHING KEY

Base colors: *Index*
1. red 0
2. purple 20
3. process blue 34

Inks:

	1.	2.	3.
Letterpress	OP-0	OP-20	OP-34
Offset	OPO-0	OPO-20	OPO-34
Gravure	OPG-0	OPG-20	OPG-34
Flexographic	OPF-0	OPF-20	OPF-34

A. group 128 plus chrome yellow

B. group 128 plus process yellow

C. group 128 plus orange

D. group 128 plus process red

E. group 128 plus brown

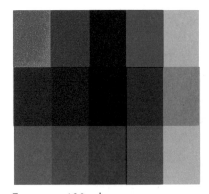

F. group 128 plus gray

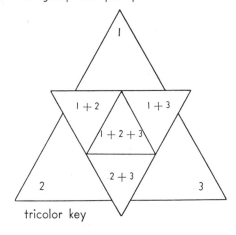

tricolor key

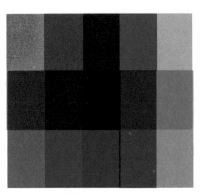

G. group 128 plus green

H. group 128 plus royal blue

MATCHING KEY

Base colors: *Index*
1. process yellow **2**
2. green **18**
3. process blue **34**

Inks:

	1.	**2.**	**3.**
Letterpress	— OP-2	OP-18	OP-34
Offset	— OPO-2	OPO-18	OPO-34
Gravure	— OPG-2	OPG-18	OPG-34
Flexographic	— OPF-2	OPF-18	OPF-34

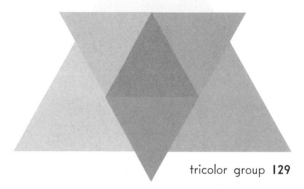

tricolor group **129**

A. group 129 plus red

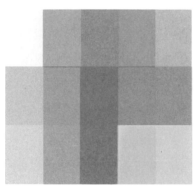

B. group 129 plus chrome yellow

C. group 129 plus orange

D. group 129 plus process red

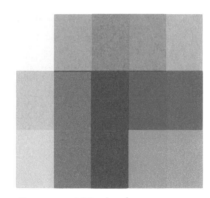

E. group 129 plus brown

F. group 129 plus gray

G. group 129 plus purple

H. group 129 plus royal blue

1	1 + 3	1 + 2 + 3	2 + 3	3
1 + 2	1 + 2 + 4	1 + 2 + 3 + 4	1 + 3 + 4	3 + 4
2	2 + 4	2 + 3 + 4	1 + 4	4

four-color key

VIEW OF CHARLOTTE AMALIE

Travel poster design by Donald E. Cooke
Color group 129A (also groups 22H, 68F, 119B)
Rendering: Plastic stylus on Bourges sheets: 70% Process Yellow, 70% Poster Red, 70% Green, 50% Process Blue.
Process: Offset. No reduction.

For strong, flat poster effect, no medium can surpass overprinting. This composition is made up of four brilliant base colors to produce the atmosphere of tropical sunshine. A certain amount of sharp angularity enhances the design quality of the picture, and dazzling light is suggested by bold contrasts.

Artists who lean to greater degrees of abstraction will find that an interlocking of color shapes in a subject of this kind will produce startling effects. For example, the device of seeing objects through other objects is easily accomplished by delineating one form over another on the various color overlays. Suggestions of such treatment may be found in the spot designs on each of the section pages dividing the warm, intermediate and cool color groups, and in the illustration on page 167.

Up to now, little has been done with overprinting in flexographic inks, using rubber plates, to produce brilliant and striking poster designs. Yet both the art medium and the printing process are made to order for the purpose. The possibilities should be thoroughly explored by anyone in the car-card, poster, or packaging fields.

Indeed, so many unexplored possibilities exist in the application of overprinting that no segment of the graphic arts industry can afford to overlook them.

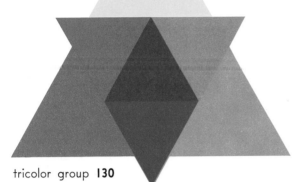

tricolor group **130**

MATCHING KEY

Base colors: *Index*
1. process yellow **2**
2. purple **20**
3. royal blue **32**

Inks:	1.	2.	3.
Letterpress —	OP-2	OP-20	OP-32
Offset —	OPO-2	OPO-20	OPO-32
Gravure —	OPG-2	OPG-20	OPG-32
Flexographic —	OPF-2	OPF-20	OPF-32

A. group 130 plus red

B. group 130 plus chrome yellow

C. group 130 plus orange

D. group 130 plus process red

E. group 130 plus brown

F. group 130 plus gray

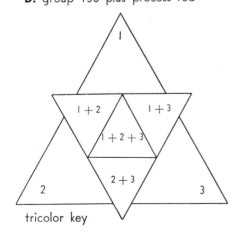

tricolor key

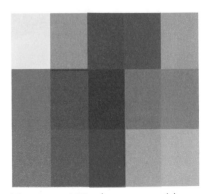

G. group 130 plus green

H. group 130 plus process blue

MATCHING KEY

Base colors: *Index*
- 1. orange **4**
- 2. green **18**
- 3. royal blue **32**

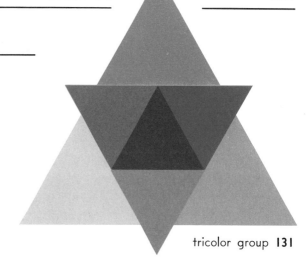

tricolor group **131**

Inks:	**1.**	**2.**	**3.**
Letterpress	OP-4	OP-18	OP-32
Offset	OPO-4	OPO-18	OPO-32
Gravure	OPG-4	OPG-18	OPG-32
Flexographic	OPF-4	OPF-18	OPF-32

A. group 131 plus red

B. group 131 plus chrome yellow

C. group 131 plus process yellow

D. group 131 plus process red

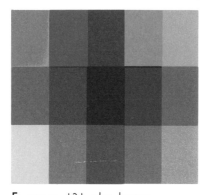

E. group 131 plus brown

F. group 131 plus gray

G. group 131 plus purple

H. group 131 plus process blue

1	1 + 3	1 + 2 + 3	2 + 3	3
1 + 2	1 + 2 + 4	1 + 2 + 3 + 4	1 + 3 + 4	3 + 4
2	2 + 4	2 + 3 + 4	1 + 4	4

four-color key

tricolor group **132**

MATCHING KEY

Base colors:		Index
1. chrome yellow	....	1
2. purple	....	20
3. process blue	....	34

Inks:	1.	2.	3.
Letterpress —	OP-1	OP-20	OP-34
Offset —	OPO-1	OPO-20	OPO-34
Gravure —	OPG-1	OPG-20	OPG-34
Flexographic —	OPF-1	OPF-20	OPF-34

A. group 132 plus red

B. group 132 plus process yellow

C. group 132 plus orange

D. group 132 plus process red

E. group 132 plus brown

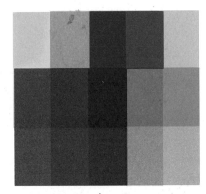

F. group 132 plus gray

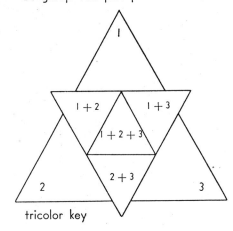

tricolor key

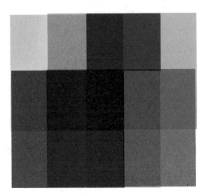

G. group 132 plus green

H. group 132 plus royal blue

MATCHING KEY

Base colors: *Index*
1. orange **4**
2. gray **17**
3. process blue **34**

Inks:	**1.**	**2.**	**3.**
Letterpress —	OP-4	OP-17	OP-34
Offset —	OPO-4	OPO-17	OPO-34
Gravure —	OPG-4	OPG-17	OPG-34
Flexographic —	OPF-4	OPF-17	OPF-34

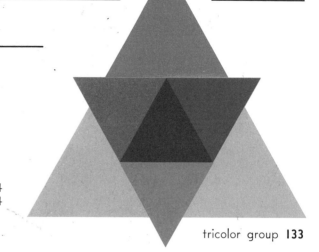

tricolor group **133**

A. group 133 plus red

B. group 133 plus chrome yellow

C. group 133 plus process yellow

D. group 133 plus process red

E. group 133 plus brown

F. group 133 plus green

G. group 133 plus purple

H. group 133 plus royal blue

1	1 + 3	1 + 2 + 3	2 + 3	3
1 + 2	1 + 2 + 4	1 + 2 + 3 + 4	1 + 3 + 4	3 + 4
2	2 + 4	2 + 3 + 4	1 + 4	4

four-color key

tricolor group **134**

MATCHING KEY

Base colors: *Index*
   1. process red **6**
   2. gray **17**
   3. royal blue **32**

Inks:	**1.**	**2.**	**3.**
Letterpress —	OP-6	OP-17	OP-32
Offset —	OPO-6	OPO-17	OPO-32
Gravure —	OPG-6	OPG-17	OPG-32
Flexographic —	OPF-6	OPF-17	OPF-32

A. group 134 plus red

B. group 134 plus chrome yellow

C. group 134 plus process yellow

D. group 134 plus orange

E. group 134 plus brown

F. group 134 plus green

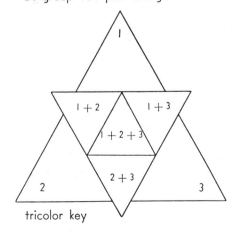

tricolor key

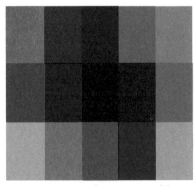

G. group 134 plus purple

H. group 134 plus process blue

COOL GROUPS

index 55 to 86

The last section of color charts contains only tricolor groups with at least two colors on the cool side of the scale (colors having an index of 17 or higher). As in the rest of the book, all grouping and indexing of colors is based upon the tricolor groups and not on the four-color combinations built from them. On each color chart page, the tricolor group is the key. It represents the common denominator for the four-color groups under it, being repeated eight times in combination with each of the other basic inks.

MATCHING KEY

Base colors: *Index*
  1. gray **17**
  2. green **18**
  3. purple **20**

Inks:	1.	2.	3.
Letterpress —	OP-17	OP-18	OP-20
Offset —	OPO-17	OPO-18	OPO-20
Gravure —	OPG-17	OPG-18	OPG-20
Flexographic —	OPF-17	OPF-18	OPF-20

tricolor group **135**

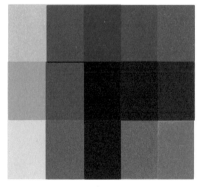

A. group 135 plus red

B. group 135 plus chrome yellow

C. group 135 plus process yellow

D. group 135 plus orange

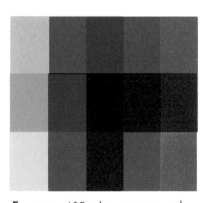

E. group 135 plus process red

F. group 135 plus brown

G. group 135 plus royal blue

H. group 135 plus process blue

1	1 + 3	1 + 2 + 3	2 + 3	3
1 + 2	1 + 2 + 4	1 + 2 + 3 + 4	1 + 3 + 4	3 + 4
2	2 + 4	2 + 3 + 4	1 + 4	4

four-color key

Key drawing rendered with a sable brush in orange showcard color as shown at right.

SENTINELS

Nature study by Donald E. Cooke
Color group 135D (also groups 87F, 93F, 97F)
Rendering: Brush and orange showcard color on illustration board; plastic stylus on Bourges sheets: 70% Green, 70% Purple, 50% Black.
Process: Offset. No reduction.

Of particular interest to artists who are adept at brush and ink, this illustration suggests a vast range of possibilities. While it retains the quality of a line overprint in the strictest sense of the term, it also employs the use of a key drawing, made on illustration board before any overlays are taped in position. In this case the key drawing was not rendered in black India ink, but in *orange showcard color,* matching the 100% Bourges Orange. Green, Purple and Gray Bourges sheets were then worked over the Orange key.

Here is a fresh solution to the problem of obtaining dry brush effects and fine lines which are almost impossible to achieve using Bourges sheets alone. The artist can delineate the finest detail, just as he would in making a pen ·or brush and ink drawing. Yet the luminosity of four overprinted colors is not lost through the application of dead black. Notice how the orange influences each of the overprinted inks. Though it is a light, brilliant color by itself, it produces all the warm darks in the picture.

Many other applications of this technique are possible. The color used for the key drawing need not match a standard Bourges color. This makes it possible for artists to create overprint visuals without relying solely on the standard overlay colors available. The key drawing might be rendered in maroon, slate blue, ocher, or any of a thousand subtle shades. In reproduction, the key plate would be printed in a transparent ink matching the color used for the key drawing. However, it should be borne in mind that any colors used should be strong enough to photograph well in line. This is particularly true of blues and grays.

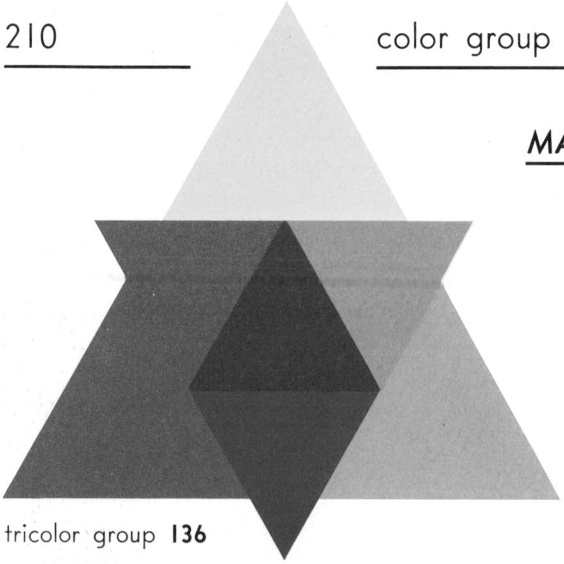

tricolor group **136**

MATCHING KEY

Base colors:

	Index
1. process yellow	**2**
2. purple	**20**
3. process blue	**34**

Inks:

	1.	**2.**	**3.**
Letterpress —	OP-2	OP-20	OP-34
Offset —	OPO-2	OPO-20	OPO-34
Gravure —	OPG-2	OPG-20	OPG-34
Flexographic —	OPF-2	OPF-20	OPF-34

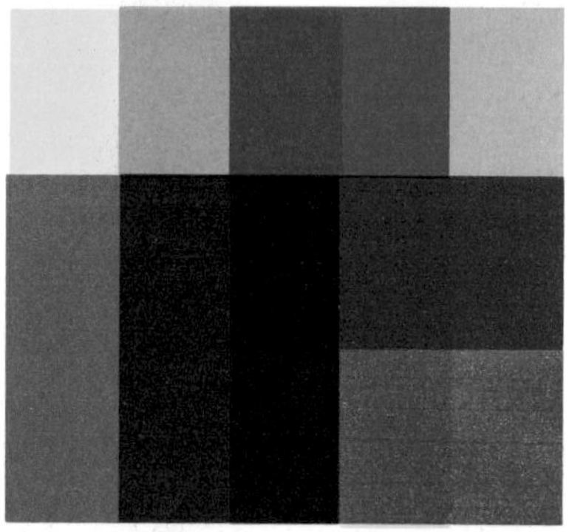

A. group 136 plus red

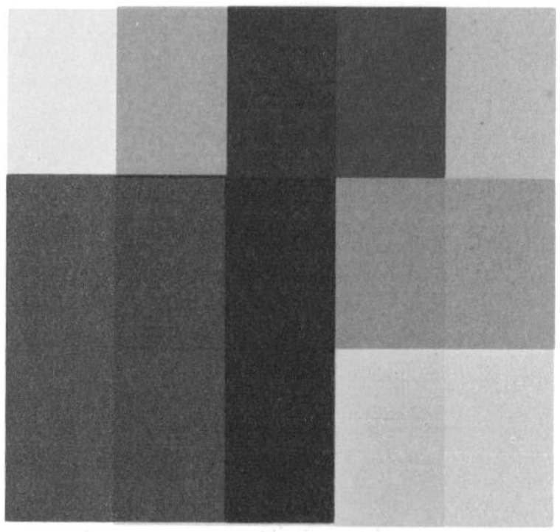

B. group 136 plus chrome yellow

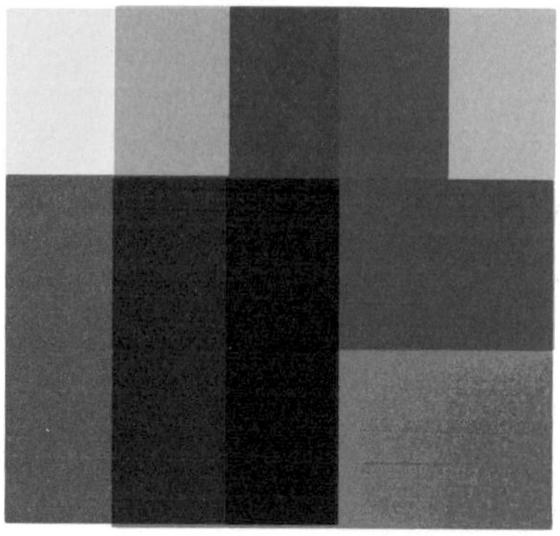

C. group 136 plus orange

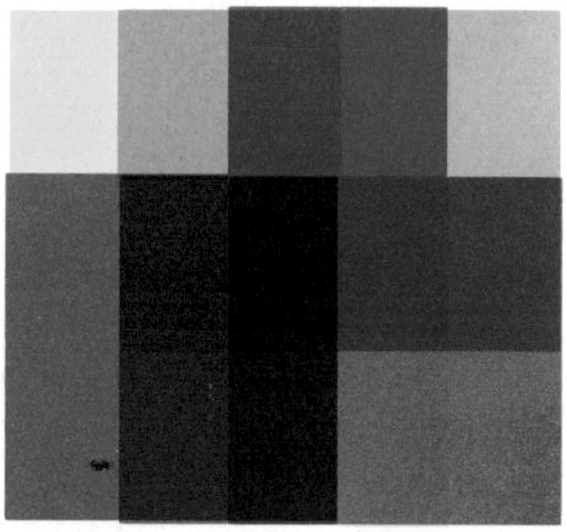

D. group 136 plus process red

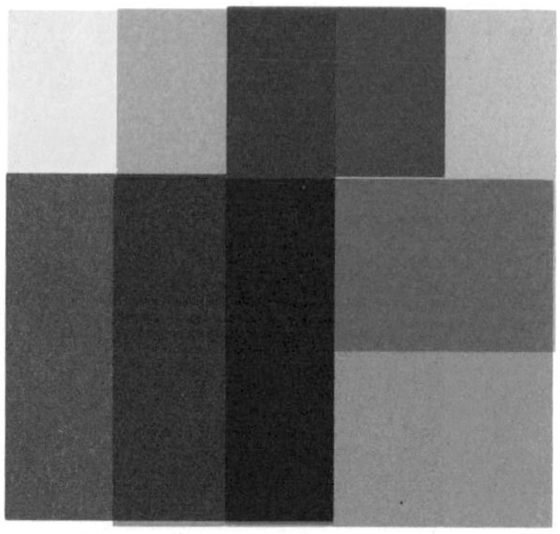

E. group 136 plus brown

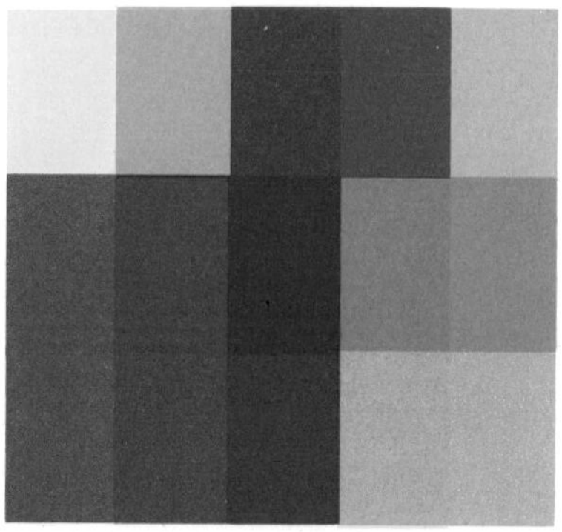

F. group 136 plus gray

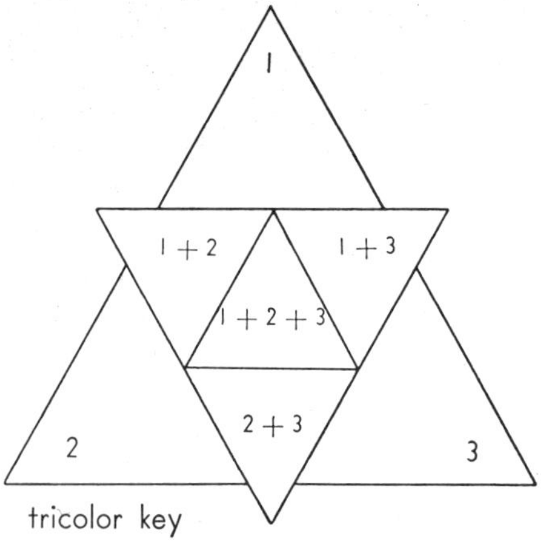

tricolor key

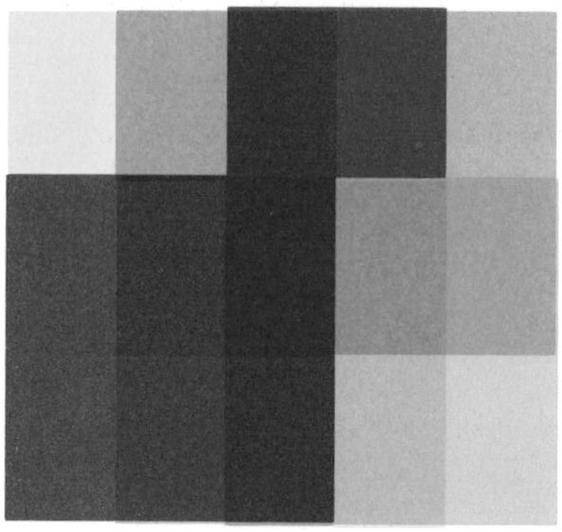

G. group 136 plus green

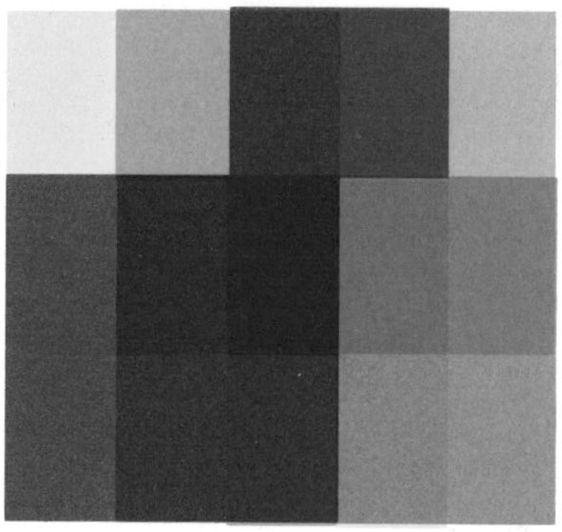

H. group 136 plus royal blue

MATCHING KEY

Base colors: *Index*
1. orange **4**
2. green **18**
3. process blue **34**

Inks:	1.	2.	3.
Letterpress	— OP-4	OP-18	OP-34
Offset	— OPO-4	OPO-18	OPO-34
Gravure	— OPG-4	OPG-18	OPG-34
Flexographic	— OPF-4	OPF-18	OPF-34

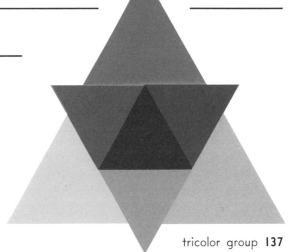

tricolor group **137**

A. group 137 plus red

B. group 137 plus chrome yellow

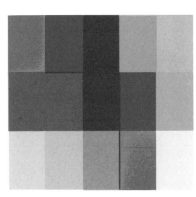

C. group 137 plus process yellow

D. group 137 plus process red

E. group 137 plus brown

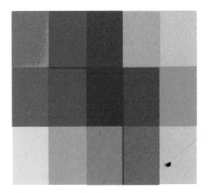

F. group 137 plus gray

G. group 137 plus purple

H. group 137 plus royal blue

1	1 + 3	1 + 2 + 3	2 + 3	3
1 + 2	1 + 2 + 4	1 + 2 + 3 + 4	1 + 3 + 4	3 + 4
2	2 + 4	2 + 3 + 4	1 + 4	4

four-color key

tricolor group **138**

MATCHING KEY

Base colors: *Index*
1. orange **4**
2. purple **20**
3. royal blue **32**

Inks:	**1.**	**2.**	**3.**
Letterpress —	OP-4	OP-20	OP-32
Offset —	OPO-4	OPO-20	OPO-32
Gravure —	OPG-4	OPG-20	OPG-32
Flexographic —	OPF-4	OPF-20	OPF-32

A. group 138 plus red

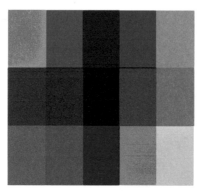

B. group 138 plus chrome yellow

C. group 138 plus process yellow

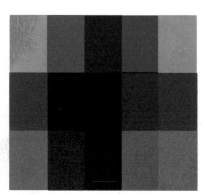

D. group 138 plus process red

E. group 138 plus brown

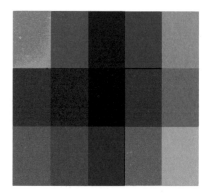

F. group 138 plus gray

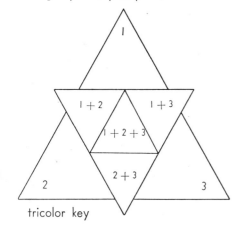

tricolor key

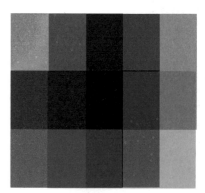

G. group 138 plus green

H. group 138 plus process blue

MATCHING KEY

Base colors: *Index*
1. process red **6**
2. green **18**
3. royal blue **32**

Inks:	**1.**	**2.**	**3.**
Letterpress	— OP-6	OP-18	OP-32
Offset	— OPO-6	OPO-18	OPO-32
Gravure	— OPG-6	OPG-18	OPG-32
Flexographic	— OPF-6	OPF-18	OPF-32

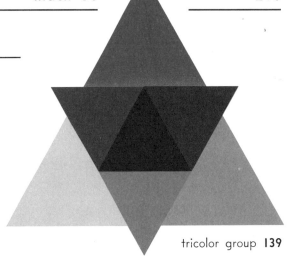

tricolor group **139**

A. group 139 plus red

B. group 139 plus chrome yellow

C. group 139 plus process yellow

D. group 139 plus orange

E. group 139 plus brown

F. group 139 plus gray

G. group 139 plus purple

H. group 139 plus process blue

1	1 + 3	1 + 2 + 3	2 + 3	3
1 + 2	1 + 2 + 4	1 + 2 + 3 + 4	1 + 3 + 4	3 + 4
2	2 + 4	2 + 3 + 4	1 + 4	4

four-color key

THE POOL

Romantic illustration by Donald E. Cooke
Color group 139D (also groups 49G, 96F, 131D)
Rendering: Plastic stylus on Bourges sheets: 100% Orange, 70% Process Red, 70% Green, 70% Poster Blue.
Process: Offset. No Reduction.

This illustration was selected for the first overprinting tests which were run during the early stages of the development of this book. Because it involved maximum over-printing of four solids, or 400% buildup of ink, it represented a calculated risk. Neither the printer, nor anyone else connected with the project, had ever attempted a reproduction of this kind, and there was considerable doubt as to whether it could be done successfully. Some technicians believed that by the time the fourth color was over-printed on a base already saturated with three solids, all sorts of printing nightmares would be encountered, such as loss of detail, offset on the backs of sheets, failure of the ink to dry properly.

A trial run went through on a two-color offset press, with the orange and process red put down first. On the second time through the press, green and royal blue were added. Although considerable offsetting occurred on coated stock, other papers be-haved well, and the results were highly satisfactory.

For the print on the opposite page, the colors were staggered so that each of the inks was dry before the next color was applied. The only difference observed in the result is a slightly deeper tone to the dark areas, probably due to the fact that no under color was disturbed by succeeding impressions.

Because letterpress printing deposits a heavier layer of ink than is generally the case in offset, it would be advisable to avoid such solid coverage in most letterpress runs. However, a study of the ink problem, judicious choice of paper, and extreme care in the presswork should bring satisfactory results by any process.

Artwise, this is an example of "subtractive" technique, where the artist starts with the dark created by four Bourges sheets and, by removing comparatively few areas in the various colors, injects light into a predominantly dark composition.

tricolor group **140**

MATCHING KEY

Base colors:			*Index*
1. process red	....		**6**
2. gray	....		**17**
3. process blue	....		**34**

Inks:	**1.**	**2.**	**3.**
Letterpress —	OP-6	OP-17	OP-34
Offset —	OPO-6	OPO-17	OPO-34
Gravure —	OPG-6	OPG-17	OPG-34
Flexographic —	OPF-6	OPF-17	OPF-34

A. group 140 plus red

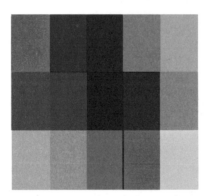

B. group 140 plus chrome yellow

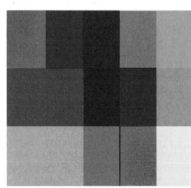

C. group 140 plus process yellow

D. group 140 plus orange

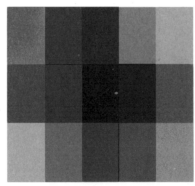

E. group 140 plus brown

F. group 140 plus green

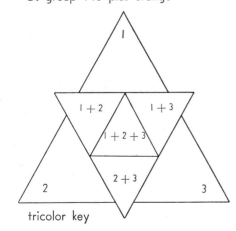

tricolor key

G. group 140 plus purple

H. group 140 plus royal blue

MATCHING KEY

Base colors: *Index*
1. orange **4**
2. purple **20**
3. process blue **34**

Inks:	**1.**	**2.**	**3.**
Letterpress —	OP-4	OP-20	OP-34
Offset —	OPO-4	OPO-20	OPO-34
Gravure —	OPG-4	OPG-20	OPG-34
Flexographic —	OPF-4	OPF-20	OPF-34

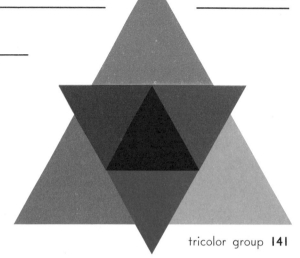

tricolor group **141**

A. group 141 plus red

B. group 141 plus chrome yellow

C. group 141 plus process yellow

D. group 141 plus process red

E. group 141 plus brown

F. group 141 plus gray

G. group 141 plus green

H. group 141 plus royal blue

1	1 + 3	1 + 2 + 3	2 + 3	3
1 + 2	1 + 2 + 4	1 + 2 + 3 + 4	1 + 3 + 4	3 + 4
2	2 + 4	2 + 3 + 4	1 + 4	4

four-color key

tricolor group **142**

MATCHING KEY

Base colors: *Index*
1. process red **6**
2. green **18**
3. process blue **34**

Inks:	1.	2.	3.
Letterpress —	OP-6	OP-18	OP-34
Offset —	OPO-6	OPO-18	OPO-34
Gravure —	OPG-6	OPG-18	OPG-34
Flexographic —	OPF-6	OPF-18	OPF-34

A. group 142 plus red

B. group 142 plus chrome yellow

C. group 142 plus process yellow

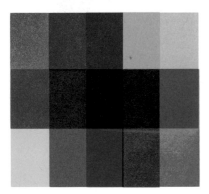

D. group 142 plus orange

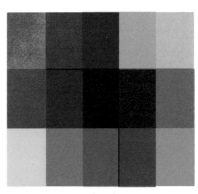

E. group 142 plus brown

F. group 142 plus gray

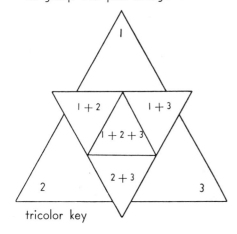

tricolor key

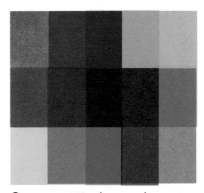

G. group 142 plus purple

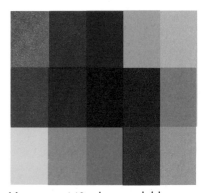

H. group 142 plus royal blue

MATCHING KEY

Base colors: *Index*
1. process red **6**
2. purple **20**
3. royal blue **32**

Inks: **1.**   **2.**   **3.**
Letterpress — OP-6   OP-20   OP-32
Offset   — OPO-6   OPO-20   OPO-32
Gravure   — OPG-6   OPG-20   OPG-32
Flexographic — OPF-6   OPF-20   OPF-32

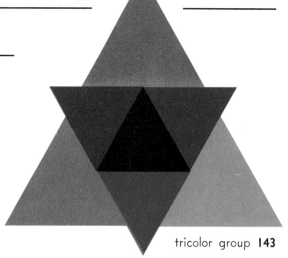

tricolor group **143**

A. group 143 plus red

B. group 143 plus chrome yellow

C. group 143 plus process yellow

D. group 143 plus orange

E. group 143 plus brown

F. group 143 plus gray

G. group 143 plus green

H. group 143 plus process blue

1	1 + 3	1 + 2 + 3	2 + 3	3
1 + 2	1 + 2 + 4	1 + 2 + 3 + 4	1 + 3 + 4	3 + 4
2	2 + 4	2 + 3 + 4	1 + 4	4

four-color key

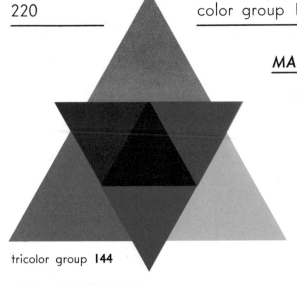

tricolor group **144**

MATCHING KEY

Base colors: *Index*
    1. process red **6**
    2. purple **20**
    3. process blue **34**

Inks:	1.	2.	3.
Letterpress —	OP-6	OP-20	OP-34
Offset —	OPO-6	OPO-20	OPO-34
Gravure —	OPG-6	OPG-20	OPG-34
Flexographic —	OPF-6	OPF-20	OPF-34

A. group 144 plus red

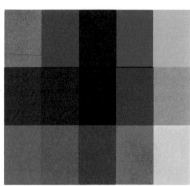

B. group 144 plus chrome yellow

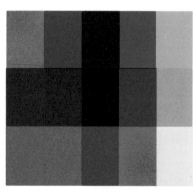

C. group 144 plus process yellow

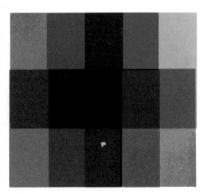

D. group 144 plus orange

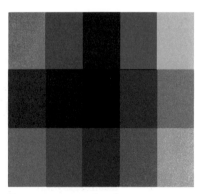

E. group 144 plus brown

F. group 144 plus gray

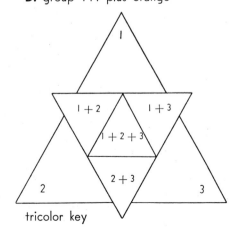

tricolor key

G. group 144 plus green

H. group 144 plus royal blue

MATCHING KEY

Base colors: *Index*
1. brown 12
2. gray 17
3. royal blue 32

Inks:

	1.	**2.**	**3.**
Letterpress	OP-12	OP-17	OP-32
Offset	OPO-12	OPO-17	OPO-32
Gravure	OPG-12	OPG-17	OPG-32
Flexographic	OPF-12	OPF-17	OPF-32

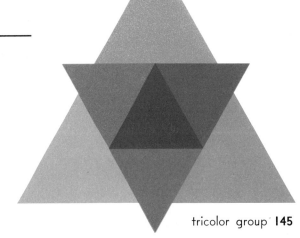

tricolor group **145**

A. group 145 plus red

B. group 145 plus chrome yellow

C. group 145 plus process yellow

D. group 145 plus orange

E. group 145 plus process red

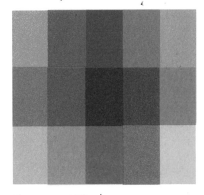

F. group 145 plus green

G. group 145 plus purple

H. group 145 plus process blue

1	1 + 3	1 + 2 + 3	2 + 3	3
1 + 2	1 + 2 + 4	1 + 2 + 3 + 4	1 + 3 + 4	3 + 4
2	2 + 4	2 + 3 + 4	1 + 4	4

four-color key

tricolor group **146**

MATCHING KEY

Base colors: *Index*
1. brown 12
2. green 18
3. royal blue 32

Inks:	**1.**	**2.**	**3.**
Letterpress —	OP-12	OP-18	OP-32
Offset —	OPO-12	OPO-18	OPO-32
Gravure —	OPG-12	OPG-18	OPG-32
Flexographic —	OPF-12	OPF-18	OPF-32

A. group 146 plus red

B. group 146 plus chrome yellow

C. group 146 plus process yellow

D. group 146 plus orange

E. group 146 plus process red

F. group 146 plus gray

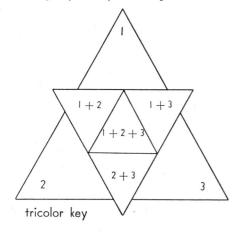

tricolor key

G. group 146 plus purple

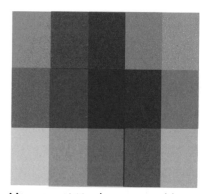

H. group 146 plus process blue

MATCHING KEY

Base colors: *Index*
1. brown **12**
2. gray **17**
3. process blue **34**

Inks: **1.**   **2.**   **3.**

	1.	2.	3.
Letterpress —	OP-12	OP-17	OP-34
Offset —	OPO-12	OPO-17	OPO-34
Gravure —	OPG-12	OPG-17	OPG-34
Flexographic —	OPF-12	OPF-17	OPF-34

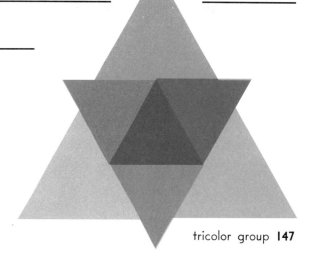

tricolor group **147**

A. group 147 plus red

B. group 147 plus chrome yellow

C. group 147 plus process yellow

D. group 147 plus orange

E. group 147 plus process red

F. group 147 plus green

G. group 147 plus purple

H. group 147 plus royal blue

1	1 + 3	1 + 2 + 3	2 + 3	3
1 + 2	1 + 2 + 4	1 + 2 + 3 + 4	1 + 3 + 4	3 + 4
2	2 + 4	2 + 3 + 4	1 + 4	4

four-color key

POWER AND LIGHT

Advertising illustration by Pennsylvania Power & Light Company
Tricolor group 147 plus black
Rendering: Key drawing, pen and India ink on illustration board. Color areas, stylus on Transopaque Red Bourges sheets, with some areas painted in Bourges red liquid.
Process: Offset. Reduction, 3 to 2.

A fine example of technical rendering and subject matter, this overprint was used as decorative design for a direct mail piece. Unlike many of the illustrations in this book, all the overlays for these colors were executed on Bourges Transopaque Red. Small facsimiles of the red color separations are shown beneath the finished print.

This method is a sort of compromise between using overlay sheets of the printing colors selected and black India ink separations. It has the advantage of transparency, making accurate registration possible, as well as ease of photographing, since red produces a line negative on standard film, sharply and accurately, without the use of filters. In the artwork, overlapping of color can be identified by the intensified red where two or more overlays are superimposed.

What it does not do, of course, is provide the artist or his client with a color visual. In simple designs, however, this is not essential. Experience with overprints, study of the color charts in this book—even experiments with swatches of Bourges sheets or colored cellophane—can be used to demonstrate the overprinted color combinations to be achieved by the finished print.

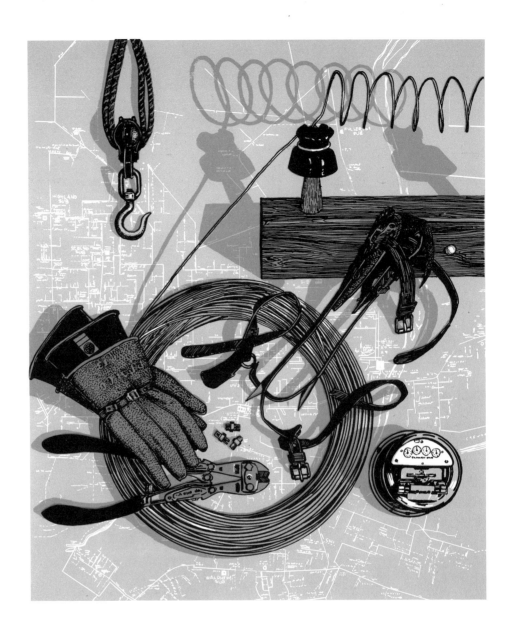

Illustration used by permission of Pennsylvania Power & Light Company.

Brown overlay

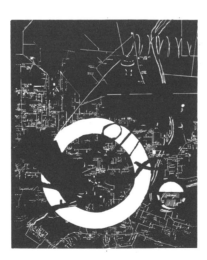
Blue overlay

Gray overlay

tricolor group **148**

MATCHING KEY

Base colors: *Index*
1. brown **12**
2. green **18**
3. process blue **34**

Inks:	1.	2.	3.
Letterpress —	OP-12	OP-18	OP-34
Offset —	OPO 12	OPO-18	OPO-34
Gravure —	OPG-12	OPG-18	OPG-34
Flexographic —	OPF-12	OPF-18	OPF-34

A. group 148 plus red

B. group 148 plus chrome yellow

C. group 148 plus process yellow

D. group 148 plus orange

E. group 148 plus process red

F. group 148 plus gray

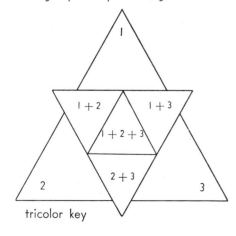

tricolor key

G. group 148 plus purple

H. group 148 plus royal blue

MATCHING KEY

Base colors: *Index*
1. brown **12**
2. purple **20**
3. royal blue **32**

Inks: **1.**   **2.**   **3.**
Letterpress   —   OP-12   OP-20   OP-32
Offset   —   OPO-12   OPO-20   OPO-32
Gravure   —   OPG-12   OPG-20   OPG-32
Flexographic   —   OPF-12   OPF-20   OPF-32

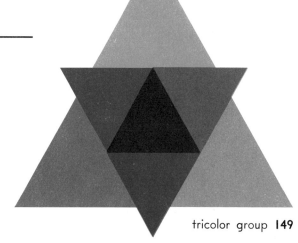

tricolor group **149**

A. group 149 plus red

B. group 149 plus chrome yellow

C. group 149 plus process yellow

D. group 149 plus orange

E. group 149 plus process red

F. group 149 plus gray

G. group 149 plus green

H. group 149 plus process blue

1	1 + 3	1 + 2 + 3	2 + 3	3
1 + 2	1 + 2 + 4	1 + 2 + 3 + 4	1 + 3 + 4	3 + 4
2	2 + 4	2 + 3 + 4	1 + 4	4

four-color key

FAITH

Documentary illustration by Albert Dorne
Tricolor group 148 plus black
Rendering: Key wash drawing on Whatman board. Color areas, plastic stylus
and Bourges color remover on Bourges sheets: 50% Brown, 70%
Green, 50% Process Blue.
Process: Offset. Reduction, 2 to 1. Overlays rendered actual size on reduced
glossy print of key drawing.

Although the combination of line and wash is not recommended as an ideal overprinting technique, this example is offered to demonstrate a means of adding color to an existing halftone painting or plate. The drawing was made originally for black and white reproduction, yet it is well suited to a simple application of color because of its strong contrasts. Overlays could be rendered over an original wash drawing, photographic print, or a reproduction proof from a halftone engraving.

In most cases of this kind, colors should be considered only as tints, and little or no attempt should be made at elaborate delineation on the line overlays. The half-tone plate itself furnishes all necessary detail.

To preserve a clear blue for the sky in Mr. Dorne's illustration, highlighting of the halftone plate background was essential, but the result in this instance is a purity of color impossible to achieve by any halftone color process.

Not all wash drawings or photographs could be successfully adapted to this type of color work. But Albert Dorne's powerful drawing, together with his use of strong light and shadow, provides clearly defined areas for the containment of solid color.

Artist: Albert Dorne
Agency: McCann-Erickson Inc.
Client: Chrysler Corporation

tricolor group **150**

MATCHING KEY

Base colors: *Index*
1. red	**0**
2. royal blue	**32**
3. process blue	**34**

Inks:

	1.	**2.**	**3.**
Letterpress —	OP-0	OP-32	OP-34
Offset —	OPO-0	OPO-32	OPO-34
Gravure —	OPG-0	OPG-32	OPG-34
Flexographic —	OPF-0	OPF-32	OPF-34

A. group 150 plus chrome yellow

B. group 150 plus process yellow

C. group 150 plus orange

D. group 150 plus process red

E. group 150 plus brown

F. group 150 plus gray

tricolor key

G. group 150 plus green

H. group 150 plus purple

MATCHING KEY

Base colors: *Index*
   1. brown **12**
   2. purple **20**
   3. process blue **34**

tricolor group 151

Inks: **1.**   **2.**   **3.**
  Letterpress — OP-12   OP-20   OP-34
  Offset   — OPO-12   OPO-20   OPO-34
  Gravure   — OPG-12   OPG-20   OPG-34
  Flexographic — OPF-12   OPF-20   OPF-34

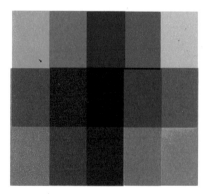

A. group 151 plus red

B. group 151 plus chrome yellow

C. group 151 plus process yellow

D. group 151 plus orange

E. group 151 plus process red

F. group 151 plus gray

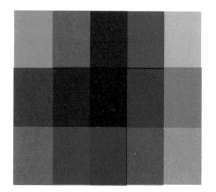

G. group 151 plus green

H. group 151 plus royal blue

1	1 + 3	1 + 2 + 3	2 + 3	3
1 + 2	1 + 2 + 4	1 + 2 + 3 + 4	1 + 3 + 4	3 + 4
2	2 + 4	2 + 3 + 4	1 + 4	4

four-color key

THE SPLENDID CENTURY

Book jacket by Douglas Gorsline, courtesy of William Sloane Associates, Inc.
Portion of tricolor group 151 plus black
Rendering: Black key, pen and India ink on illustration board. Color areas, stylus on Bourges sheets: 50% Orange, 70% Process Blue.
Process: Offset. Reduction, 3 to 2.

Douglas Gorsline is one of America's foremost authorities on historic costume, as well as an accomplished illustrator. In the accompanying book jacket we see a superb combination of his knowledge and talent, for in this type of subject Gorsline is at his best.

Typical of his delicate pen-line treatments, the key drawing seems nevertheless to be an integral part of the boldly rendered solid-color areas. This welding of delicate black line and broadly applied tints is accomplished by an intelligent selection and use of two harmonious colors which produce a pleasing neutral overprint. Everything holds its place. Neither the application of color nor the painstaking detail of the drawing is overemphasized.

Remarkable, too, for its low reproduction cost, the design would be no more effective in full color. Four colors are achieved with three line plates, the very treatment of which is perfectly in keeping with the period portrayed.

Since the brown of COLOR BY OVERPRINTING is very similar to the pale orange of the jacket's original printing, it is used here rather than the vivid full-strength orange of the basic inks.

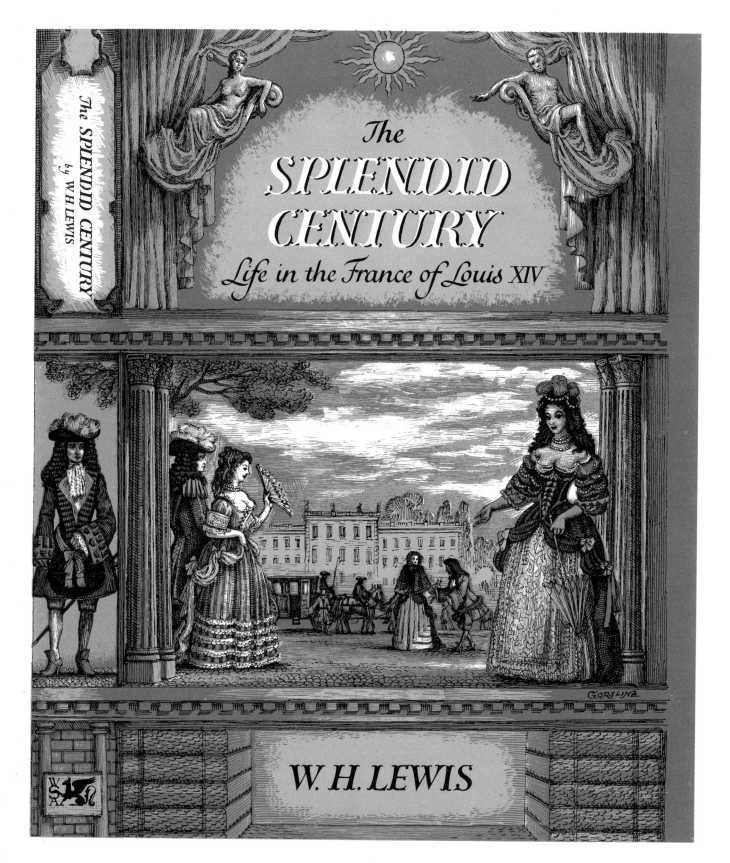

The

SPLENDID CENTURY

Life in the France of Louis XIV

W. H. LEWIS

tricolor group **152**

MATCHING KEY

Base colors:			*Index*
1. chrome yellow			**1**
2. royal blue			**32**
3. process blue			**34**

Inks:	**1.**	**2.**	**3.**
Letterpress —	OP-1	OP-32	OP-34
Offset —	OPO-1	OPO-32	OPO-34
Gravure —	OPG-1	OPG-32	OPG-34
Flexographic —	OPF-1	OPF-32	OPF-34

A. group 152 plus red

B. group 152 plus process yellow

C. group 152 plus orange

D. group 152 plus process red

E. group 152 plus brown

F. group 152 plus gray

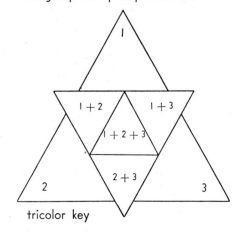

tricolor key

G. group 152 plus green

H. group 152 plus purple

MATCHING KEY

Base colors: *Index*
1. gray **17**
2. green **18**
3. royal blue **32**

Inks:	**1.**	**2.**	**3.**
Letterpress —	OP-17	OP-18	OP-32
Offset —	OPO-17	OPO-18	OPO-32
Gravure —	OPG-17	OPG-18	OPG-32
Flexographic —	OPF-17	OPF-18	OPF-32

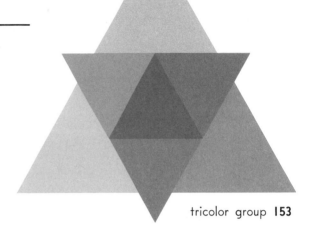

tricolor group **153**

A. group 153 plus red

B. group 153 plus chrome yellow

C. group 153 plus process yellow

D. group 153 plus orange

E. group 153 plus process red

F. group 153 plus brown

G. group 153 plus purple

H. group 153 plus process blue

1	1 + 3	1 + 2 + 3	2 + 3	3
1 + 2	1 + 2 + 4	1 + 2 + 3 + 4	1 + 3 + 4	3 + 4
2	2 + 4	2 + 3 + 4	1 + 4	4

four-color key

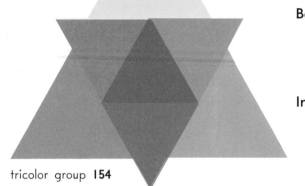

tricolor group **154**

MATCHING KEY

Base colors: *Index*
1. process yellow **2**
2. royal blue **32**
3. process blue **34**

Inks:	1.	2.	3.
Letterpress —	OP-2	OP-32	OP-34
Offset —	OPO-2	OPO-32	OPO-34
Gravure —	OPG-2	OPG-32	OPG-34
Flexographic —	OPF-2	OPF-32	OPF-34

A. group 154 plus red

B. group 154 plus chrome yellow

C. group 154 plus orange

D. group 154 plus process red

E. group 154 plus brown

F. group 154 plus gray

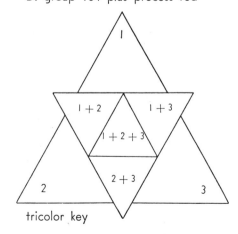

tricolor key

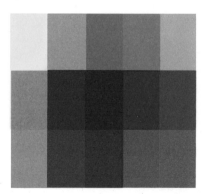

G. group 154 plus green

H. group 154 plus purple

MATCHING KEY

Base colors: *Index*
     1. gray **17**
     2. green **18**
     3. process blue **34**

Inks:	**1.**	**2.**	**3.**
Letterpress	OP-17	OP-18	OP-34
Offset	OPO-17	OPO-18	OPO-34
Gravure	OPG-17	OPG-18	OPG-34
Flexographic	OPF-17	OPF-18	OPF-34

tricolor group **155**

A. group 155 plus red

B. group 155 plus chrome yellow

C. group 155 plus process yellow

D. group 155 plus orange

E. group 155 plus process red

F. group 155 plus brown

G. group 155 plus purple

H. group 155 plus royal blue

1	1 + 3	1 + 2 + 3	2 + 3	3
1 + 2	1 + 2 + 4	1 + 2 + 3 + 4	1 + 3 + 4	3 + 4
2	2 + 4	2 + 3 + 4	1 + 4	4

four-color key

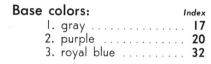

tricolor group **156**

MATCHING KEY

Base colors: *Index*
1. gray **17**
2. purple **20**
3. royal blue **32**

Inks:	**1.**	**2.**	**3.**
Letterpress —	OP-17	OP-20	OP-32
Offset —	OPO-17	OPO-20	OPO-32
Gravure —	OPG-17	OPG-20	OPG-32
Flexographic —	OPF-17	OPF-20	OPF-32

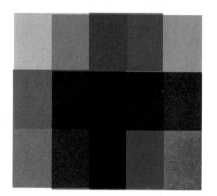

A. group 156 plus red

B. group 156 plus chrome yellow

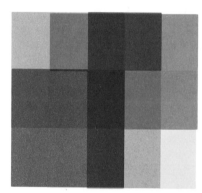

C. group 156 plus process yellow

D. group 156 plus orange

E. group 156 plus process red

F. group 156 plus brown

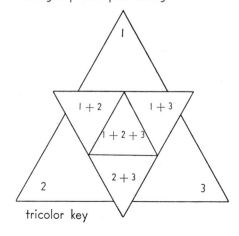

tricolor key

G. group 156 plus green

H. group 156 plus process blue

MATCHING KEY

Base colors: *Index*
1. orange **4**
2. royal blue **32**
3. process blue **34**

Inks:	1.	2.	3.
Letterpress —	OP-4	OP-32	OP-34
Offset —	OPO-4	OPO-32	OPO-34
Gravure —	OPG-4	OPG-32	OPG-34
Flexographic —	OPF-4	OPF-32	OPF-34

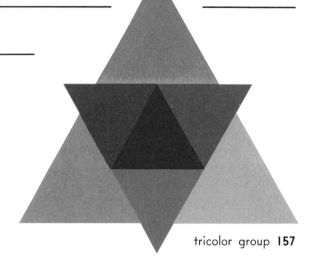

tricolor group **157**

A. group 157 plus red

B. group 157 plus chrome yellow

C. group 157 plus process yellow

D. group 157 plus process red

E. group 157 plus brown

F. group 157 plus gray

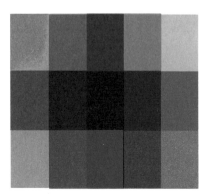

G. group 157 plus green

H. group 157 plus purple

1	1 + 3	1 + 2 + 3	2 + 3	3
1 + 2	1 + 2 + 4	1 + 2 + 3 + 4	1 + 3 + 4	3 + 4
2	2 + 4	2 + 3 + 4	1 + 4	4

four-color key

tricolor group **158**

MATCHING KEY

Base colors:			Index
1. green			**18**
2. purple			**20**
3. royal blue			**32**

Inks:	1.	2.	3.
Letterpress —	OP-18	OP-20	OP-32
Offset —	OPO-18	OPO-20	OPO-32
Gravure —	OPG-18	OPG-20	OPG-32
Flexographic —	OPF-18	OPF-20	OPF-32

A. group 158 plus red

B. group 158 plus chrome yellow

C. group 158 plus process yellow

D. group 158 plus orange

E. group 158 plus process red

F. group 158 plus brown

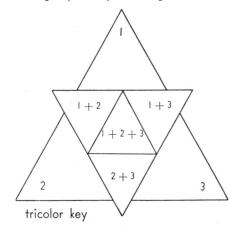

tricolor key

G. group 158 plus gray

H. group 158 plus process blue

MATCHING KEY

Base colors: *Index*
1. gray 17
2. purple 20
3. process blue 34

Inks: **1.**   **2.**   **3.**

	1.	2.	3.
Letterpress	OP-17	OP-20	OP-34
Offset	OPO-17	OPO-20	OPO-34
Gravure	OPG-17	OPG-20	OPG-34
Flexographic	OPF-17	OPF-20	OPF-34

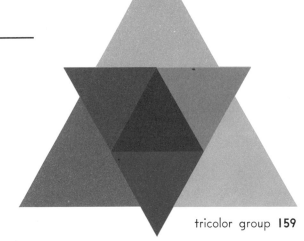

tricolor group **159**

A. group 159 plus red

B. group 159 plus chrome yellow

C. group 159 plus process yellow

D. group 159 plus orange

E. group 159 plus process red

F. group 159 plus brown

G. group 159 plus green

H. group 159 plus royal blue

1	1 + 3	1 + 2 + 3	2 + 3	3
1 + 2	1 + 2 + 4	1 + 2 + 3 + 4	1 + 3 + 4	3 + 4
2	2 + 4	2 + 3 + 4	1 + 4	4

four-color key

WINTER AFTERNOON

Landscape by Donald E. Cooke
Color group 159D (also groups 93H, 133G, 141F)
Rendering: Bourges color remover and plastic stylus on Bourges sheets: 100% Orange, 50% Process Blue, 70% Purple, 50% Black.
Process: Offset. No reduction.

Three cool colors combined with brilliant orange are ideal for this snow scene. Since one of the inks is gray, the picture could be reproduced in a press run which required black, simply by using a 50% screened tint when making the plate from the gray Bourges overlay. (See also illustrations on pages 42 and 43.)

In this rendering, most detailed delineation of trees, figures, houses and so forth, was worked on the orange overlay. Dark lines and masses result when any one or any combination of the other three colors is superimposed over the orange "key." For even sharper detail in an orange key, see the illustration on page 209, where the base consisted of a brush drawing in orange showcard color on illustration board.

On the overlay art for *Winter Afternoon*, it was found that removal of the gray plate would make no change in the basic drawing, but would transform the time of the scene to midday, instead of late afternoon. Without the gray, the sky becomes a clear, cloudless blue, while the rest of the composition retains the heightened color of broad daylight. Such experiments with Bourges overlay art sometimes result in new discoveries, or varied printing applications of the same design. It is always worth testing the finished art in its various color components to see if some unexpected result may be achieved with fewer colors than called for in the original plan.

tricolor group **160**

MATCHING KEY

Base colors: *Index*
1. process red **6**
2. royal blue **32**
3. process blue **34**

Inks:	**1.**	**2.**	**3.**
Letterpress — OP-6		OP-32	OP-34
Offset — OPO-6		OPO-32	OPO-34
Gravure — OPG-6		OPG-32	OPG-34
Flexographic — OPF-6		OPF-32	OPF-34

A. group 160 plus red

B. group 160 plus chrome yellow

C. group 160 plus process yellow

D. group 160 plus orange

E. group 160 plus brown

F. group 160 plus gray

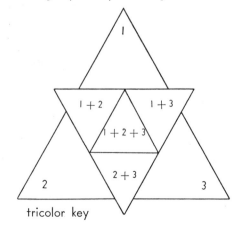

tricolor key

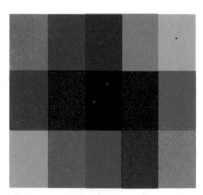

G. group 160 plus green

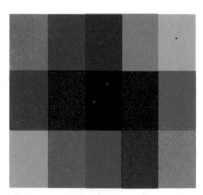

H. group 160 plus purple

MATCHING KEY

Base colors: *Index*
1. green 18
2. purple 20
3. process blue 34

Inks:

	1.	**2.**	**3.**
Letterpress	— OP-18	OP-20	OP-34
Offset	— OPO-18	OPO-20	OPO-34
Gravure	— OPG-18	OPG-20	OPG-34
Flexographic	— OPF-18	OPF-20	OPF-34

tricolor group **161**

A. group 161 plus red

B. group 161 plus chrome yellow

C. group 161 plus process yellow

D. group 161 plus orange

E. group 161 plus process red

F. group 161 plus brown

G. group 161 plus gray

H. group 161 plus royal blue

1	1 + 3	1 + 2 + 3	2 + 3	3
1 + 2	1 + 2 + 4	1 + 2 + 3 + 4	1 + 3 + 4	3 + 4
2	2 + 4	2 + 3 + 4	1 + 4	4

four-color key

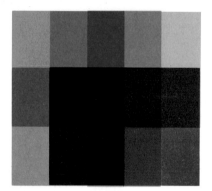

tricolor group **162**

MATCHING KEY

Base colors:　　　　*Index*
1. brown **12**
2. royal blue **32**
3. process blue **34**

Inks:	**1.**	**2.**	**3.**
Letterpress —	OP-12	OP-32	OP-34
Offset —	OPO-12	OPO-32	OPO-34
Gravure —	OPG-12	OPG-32	OPG-34
Flexographic —	OPF-12	OPF-32	OPF-34

A. group 162 plus red

B. group 162 plus chrome yellow

C. group 162 plus process yellow

D. group 162 plus orange

E. group 162 plus process red

F. group 162 plus gray

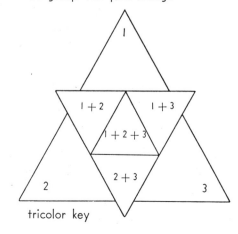

tricolor key

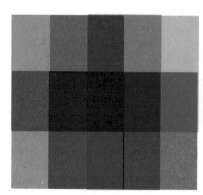

G. group 162 plus green

H. group 162 plus purple

MATCHING KEY

Base colors: *Index*
1. gray 17
2. royal blue 32
3. process blue 34

Inks: **1.**   **2.**   **3.**

	1.	2.	3.
Letterpress	OP-17	OP-32	OP-34
Offset	OPO-17	OPO-32	OPO-34
Gravure	OPG-17	OPG-32	OPG-34
Flexographic	OPF-17	OPF-32	OPF-34

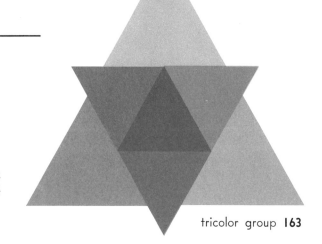

tricolor group **163**

A. group 163 plus red

B. group 163 plus chrome yellow

C. group 163 plus process yellow

D. group 163 plus orange

E. group 163 plus process red

F. group 163 plus brown

G. group 163 plus green

H. group 163 plus purple

1	1 + 3	1 + 2 + 3	2 + 3	3
1 + 2	1 + 2 + 4	1 + 2 + 3 + 4	1 + 3 + 4	3 + 4
2	2 + 4	2 + 3 + 4	1 + 4	4

four-color key

tricolor group **164**

MATCHING KEY

Base colors:		*Index*	
1. green		**18**	
2. royal blue		**32**	
3. process blue		**34**	

Inks:	**1.**	**2.**	**3.**
Letterpress —	OP-18	OP-32	OP-34
Offset —	OPO-18	OPO-32	OPO-34
Gravure —	OPG-18	OPG-32	OPG-34
Flexographic —	OPF-18	OPF-32	OPF-34

A. group 164 plus red

B. group 164 plus chrome yellow

C. group 164 plus process yellow

D. group 164 plus orange

E. group 164 plus process red

F. group 164 plus brown

tricolor key

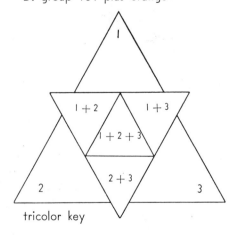

G. group 164 plus gray

H. group 164 plus purple

MATCHING KEY

Base colors: *Index*
1. purple **20**
2. royal blue **32**
3. process blue **34**

Inks:	1.	2.	3.
Letterpress	OP-20	OP-32	OP-34
Offset	OPO-20	OPO-32	OPO-34
Gravure	OPG-20	OPG-32	OPG-34
Flexographic	OPF-20	OPF-32	OPF-34

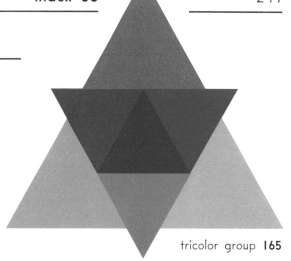

tricolor group **165**

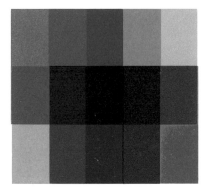

A. group 165 plus red

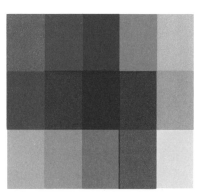

B. group 165 plus chrome yellow

C. group 165 plus process yellow

D. group 165 plus orange

E. group 165 plus process red

F. group 165 plus brown

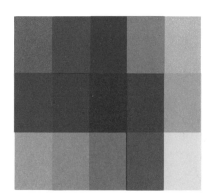

G. group 165 plus gray

H. group 165 plus green

1	1 + 3	1 + 2 + 3	2 + 3	3
1 + 2	1 + 2 + 4	1 + 2 + 3 + 4	1 + 3 + 4	3 + 4
2	2 + 4	2 + 3 + 4	1 + 4	4

four-color key

ACKNOWLEDGMENTS

No book can be made without the combined contributions and skills of many people. Though it is almost impossible to list everyone who helped to produce COLOR BY OVERPRINTING, nevertheless, in addition to those artists who contributed illustrations, special thanks are due to the following:

Harold G. Bensing
James J. Deeney
Bensing Brothers and Deeney, Inc.

Arthur Schaffert
Robert H. Blattner
The Reader's Digest

William B. Smith
National Advertising Manufacturing Company

Mrs. Jean Bourges Mayfield
Bourges, Inc.

Walliston K. James
Philadelphia-Weeks Engraving Company

Austin J. Bailey
The Holliston Mills, Inc.

During three solid years of preparation, the project could easily have foundered many times without the untiring efforts of Charles W. Abadie, who fought as many battles and died as many deaths as the author in his desire to see it through. Others whose advice and encouragement proved invaluable include Frederic S. Balch, Edward M. Wade, Sigurd W. Haug, Frank A. Hamel, Jr., Miriam Schwartz, Thomas C. Bayruns, Jack I. Nass, and Edwin J. Schoettle, Jr.

It must be said, too, that the publishers showed exceptional courage to launch an undertaking of such magnitude in view of the fact that so much in the realm of overprinting was unknown at the outset. I am especially indebted to Charles F. Kindt, Jr., President; and Parke H. Lutz, Executive Vice President of The John C. Winston Company.

To George Kimber belongs the credit for outstanding production management of one of the most involved book projects ever developed.

Valuable contributions have been made by Frank Ferrigno, offset plant superintendent; James L. Smith, production supervisor; Richard Englander, foreman, stripping department; Milton Williams, cameraman; Joseph Kneble, stripper; Anthony Ferrigno, platemaker; Walter P. Buczko and Charles Klevence, pressmen. Their tireless supervision of the film stripping and the twelve-color press run required weeks of painstaking attention to detail.

I could scarcely overlook the copy editors, Laura M. Arnold and Mary Solak; or Evelyn Kudrey, my secretary, who by now must know as much about overprinting as anyone in graphic arts, and who handled voluminous correspondence so expertly for this project.

Finally, I wish to pay tribute to my teacher—Henry C. Pitz, whose course in illustration at the Philadelphia Museum School of Art has started many a young artist on a happy and successful career.

D.E.C.